PATTERNS OF MUSCULAR ACTIVITY
IN SELECTED SPORT SKILLS

PATTERNS OF MUSCULAR ACTIVITY IN SELECTED SPORT SKILLS

An Electromyographic Study

By

MARION R. BROER, Ph.D.

Professor of Physical Education
University of Washington
Seattle, Washington

and

SARA JANE HOUTZ, M.S.

Research and Educational Consultant
Detroit Orthopedic Clinic
Detroit, Michigan

CHARLES C THOMAS • PUBLISHER
Springfield • Illinois • U.S.A.

Published and Distributed Throughout the World by
CHARLES C THOMAS • PUBLISHER
BANNERSTONE HOUSE
301-327 East Lawrence Avenue, Springfield, Illinois, U.S.A.
NATCHEZ PLANTATION HOUSE
735 North Atlantic Boulevard, Fort Lauderdale, Florida, U.S.A.

*With THOMAS BOOKS careful attention is given to all details of
manufacturing and design. It is the Publisher's desire to present books
that are satisfactory as to their physical qualities and artistic possibilities
and appropriate for their particular use. THOMAS BOOKS will be true
to those laws of quality that assure a good name and good will.*

Printed in the United States of America
AA-S-4

Preface

THIS INVESTIGATION is the cooperative effort of representatives of two closely related professions, Physical Education and Physical Therapy. In general, investigators studying the movement of normal persons and those interested in the movement problems of persons with neuromuscular or orthopedic impairment seem to have taken divergent paths. Nevertheless, the same basic knowledge is important to both. A clear understanding of the functioning of normal muscles is equally essential to the physical educator teaching the normal person and to the physical therapist working with the handicapped.

The complexity of this first attempt to sample muscles of the entire body during the performance of complex motor skills makes detailed analysis almost impossible. Because of this, and the fact that so many muscles act over more than one joint, other kinesiologists may make somewhat different interpretations of the data that are presented. However, it is the hope of the authors that this monograph will increase the understanding of the way in which normal muscles function together, and that it will serve as a background against which the results of more detailed investigations of single muscles or small groups of muscles will take on greater meaning, and thus expand the knowledge that can be gained from these studies. In this way, it should assist both the physical educator and the physical therapist with the solution of normal and abnormal movement problems.

This study could not have been accomplished without the cooperation of the School of Physical and Health Education, Department for Women, University of Washington and the Detroit Orthopedic Clinic, as well as an Amy Morris Homans grant from Wellesley College. The Detroit Orthopedic Clinic is a nonprofit agency supported by the United Foundation of Detroit. The Research and Education Department of this agency is supported only by special grant funds. These were received from the Sigma Gamma Foundation, Sigma Gamma Association, Omega Eta Tau, D. M. Ferry, Jr. Trustee Corporation, Kresge Foundation, Ford Motor Company Fund, and Eph Foundation.

We express sincere appreciation to Miss M. Genevieve Blakeley, Executive Director of the Detroit Orthopedic Clinic for making this study possible; to Miss Elizabeth Culver, who participated as the subject; to Mrs.

Sammie Lou Gilbert, Research Aide, for her technical aide, and to Misses Sheila Walsh, Susan Cerre, and Susan Bayer, who volunteered to assist in the collection of the data.

MARION R. BROER
SARA JANE HOUTZ

Contents

		Page
Preface	....	v

Chapter

I.	INTRODUCTION	3
	Purpose	3
	Delimitations	3
	Limitations	4
II.	RELATED LITERATURE	5
III.	METHODS AND PROCEDURES	8
IV.	UNDERHAND PATTERN	12
	Underhand Throw	12
	Volleyball Serve	18
	Badminton Serve	23
	Bowling	28
V.	OVERHAND PATTERN	35
	Overhand Throw	35
	Badminton Clear	42
	Tennis Serve	48
VI.	SIDEARM PATTERN	53
	Basketball Throw	53
	Tennis Drive	58
	Batting	62
	Golf	68
VII.	COMPARISON OF THE THREE THROWS	76
VIII.	ONE-FOOT JUMP	77
	Volleyball Spike	77
	Basketball Lay-up	83
IX.	GENERAL OBSERVATIONS	89
	Bibliography	91

PATTERNS OF MUSCULAR ACTIVITY
IN SELECTED SPORT SKILLS

Chapter I

Introduction

ELECTROMYOGRAPHY is a technique which picks up, amplifies, and records minute electrical activity in a muscle. Various methods are used for obtaining action potentials. In general, for diagnostic purposes of muscle pathology, needle or wire electrodes are inserted into the muscles and the electrical activity is recorded on an oscillograph. Surface electrodes placed on the skin over the belly of the muscle record the summation of action potentials beneath and between the electrodes. A multi-channel ink-writing dynograph permits the simultaneous recording of patterns of electrical activity of a number of muscles and thus it is possible to study the timing of action potentials as various muscles participate in a complex movement. Although the magnitude of the action potential of one muscle cannot be compared to that of another muscle, the relative magnitude of a single muscle at various times during the performance of a single skill, or various skills, can be studied.

This type of recording is an accepted method for studying surface muscles.

This monograph presents an electromyographic study of coordinated muscle function of all body segments during the performance of selected complex skills fundamental to sport activities. To date, electromyographic studies have been limited primarily to a group (or groups) of muscles which function around a single or adjacent joints, and usually to more or less simple movements. A few investigations of the action of single or adjacent joints during the performance of sport skills have been published also, but none has attempted to study the coordination of the various body segments. The more comprehensive analyses of complex skills have been accomplished with the use of still and motion pictures. Analysis of pictures has indicated that there appear to be some basic movement patterns which are common to various sport skills.

PURPOSE

The primary purpose of this study was to determine whether there are patterns of muscle function common to various complex sport skills. A further purpose was to analyze the activity of the muscles sampled during the performance of the sport skills by a normal, well-skilled adult female.

DELIMITATIONS

The above purpose demanded the study of many muscles representing all segments of the body and various sport skills. The study was limited to thirteen different sport skills and to the sixty-eight muscles which were believed to be most accessible for study by surface electrodes. To obtain a composite picture of the activity of sixty-eight muscles during the performance of this number of skills, the study was limited to one subject.

LIMITATIONS

It is possible to determine whether there are movement patterns which are common to various skills with one subject since the electrode placement was constant for the entire series of activities. Muscle function during the performance of simple movements was recorded so that this subject could be compared to previous studies in order to reduce the limiting effects of one subject on the accomplishment of the second purpose of the study.

The authors recognize that certain limitations are inherent in the use of surface electrodes and in the study of one subject.

It is recognized that such factors as body build, skill level, and fatigue may influence magnitude and pattern of muscle activity. Although studies of isolated muscles (or groups of muscles) during simple movements have indicated that the general pattern of contraction is usually similar in normal individuals, skill level could effect muscle action in more complex coordinations. These results, therefore, are limited to a skilled level of performance. Fatigue did not enter into the results since frequent rest periods were interposed and the study was extended over a period of two weeks with not more than approximately two one-hour periods of recording a day on four days of each week. At no time was the subject fatigued.

Chapter II

Related Literature

INNUMERABLE electromyographic studies of selected muscle groups during the performance of a variety of movements have been published. Both Joseph and Basmajian have summarized electromyographic literature ·and contributed extensively to the understanding of muscle function during movement. No attempt is made to duplicate the inclusive bibliographies presented in their two books. However, a few references applicable to this study are included. Electromyograms during simple range of movements of the subject for this study were compared with like data published in the literature and were found to be identical or very similar.

Electrical activity of the shoulder girdle muscles, either singly or in groups, has been studied by several investigators. Yamshon and Bierman studied the trapezius (1948) and the deltoid (1949). Reeder investigated the function of the latissimus dorsi, while Inman, Close, and Saha studied the composite activity of the muscles acting on the shoulder girdle and arm during simple range of movements. Their findings in general confirm the kinesiologist's description of muscle function.

Slater-Hammel (1949) studied shoulder girdle muscles acting on the arm during the tennis stroke. Although there was some variability in the pattern of the five subjects studied, he found that during the forward swing, the pectoralis major, anterior deltoid, and biceps were active in all subjects, the latissimus dorsi in three, the triceps in four, and the middle deltoid in one. Although the ball was suspended, the results are similar to the findings in this study (p. 61). The same investigator (1948) studied muscles acting on the arm during the golf stroke. During the driving phase, he found electrical activity in the left biceps, right and left triceps, and right latissimus dorsi of all subjects, and in the right pectoralis major and left posterior deltoid of three subjects. Although there were no electromyograms for comparison, these muscles were active in this study (p. 70).

Kitzman studied the right and left pectoralis major, triceps, and latissimus dorsi during the batting of a suspended ball. He reported that most of the action potentials occurred in the backswing and there was little, if any, activity in these muscles during the forward swing. These results do not appear to be reasonable and are not substantiated by the findings of this study (p. 65).

Hellebrandt and co-workers (1955) studied the muscles acting on the shoulder girdle and arm during ballistic movements. During antero-posterior swinging of the upper extremity, momentum of the forward swing was decelerated by action of the teres major, latissimus dorsi, and triceps, while the anterior deltoid, pectoralis major, teres major, and middle deltoid were active in the posterior swing. This type of ballistic movement is relatively uncommon in sport activities, although in the study herein reported there appeared to be a checking action of these muscles when momentum was a factor. Studies from the same laboratory (1957) also demonstrated the action of the pectoralis major, deltoid, trapezius, and latissimus dorsi during selected subtests of the Minnesota Rate of Manipulation test. One subtest, placing, involved forward flexion of the arm grasping the light disc, retraction of the arm, and release of the object. In essence, the anterior deltoid and, to a lesser degree, the clavicular portion of the pectoralis major were active as forward flexors of the arm. The lower trapezius stabilized the scapula and the middle deltoid maintained slight abduction of the arm. Gravity apparently retracted the arm with possibly minor assistance from the posterior deltoid. In two other investigations (1956) from the same laboratory, widespread activity in the upper arm, shoulder girdle, abdominal and back muscles occurred during severe wrist flexion and extension exercises. This would indicate that the greater the stress in a sport skill, the greater the magnitude of response and the larger the number of muscles recruited.

Muscles acting on the forearm, wrist and/or hand have been studied by Gellhorn, Bierman and Yamshon, Slaughter, Nakamura *et al.*, Santo, Long, and Brown. Bierman and Yamshon demonstrated electrical activity in the biceps during elbow flexion with the forearm in supination, mid-position, or pronation. They also demonstrated activity during forward flexion of the arm. Nakamura demonstrated activity in both finger flexors and extensors during grasping an object. The magnitude of electrical activity in both extensors and flexors showed marked increase when the object was 3.0 cm across and 1.0 kg in weight. Long and Brown confirmed the observation by Nakamura that both flexors and extensors were active when the subject made a fist.

A study of the abdominal muscles by Partridge and Walters confirmed the previous investigations by Floyd and Silver (1950) and Allen. All found that these muscles were active as a standing subject leaned backward, but not as he forward flexed the trunk. It is obvious that gravity is the force affecting the backward and forward movement of the trunk, and the abdominal muscles are involved in opposing gravity during the lean backward. If the subject forward flexed the trunk only to the point where the stretching of the back and hip muscles and ligaments stopped the movement, the abdominal muscles were not active. An effort to further flex the trunk increased potentials in the abdominal muscles as they acted to overcome resistance within the body. When the subject in this study forward flexed the trunk, no activity was recorded in the rectus abdominis until she made an extreme effort to gain maximum flexion. A comparison of the action potential patterns of the rectus abdominis and external obliques during the golf swing in this study (p. 72) shows timing and magnitude similar to that published by Partridge and Walters. The speed of recording paper was faster in the previous study and therefore the electromyogram is spread over a greater distance. These authors and Campbell demonstrated muscle activity during certain respiratory movements. Without doubt, some of the muscular activity seen in the records of this study was caused by respiration. No attempt has been made to analyze this in the discussion of the various skills, although it is recognized to be a factor in muscles of respiration.

Portnoy and Morin studied the sacrospinalis, hamstrings, gastrocnemius, and quadriceps as the standing subject shifted his weight forward and as he flexed the trunk forward. Their results confirmed the previous work by Allen and Floyd and Silver (1951, 1955), who studied the sacrospinalis, and Joseph and Houtz (1964), who studied the thigh and leg muscles. These studies demonstrated increased activity in the sacrospinalis, hamstrings, and gastrocnemius as the weight was moved forward or the trunk flexed anteriorly. Increased electrical activity was evident in the sacrospinalis and hamstrings when the extended arms were flexed forward and, in the supporting lower extremity, when standing on one foot. In the present study, the same results were obvious when the subject performed simple forward flexion and during her performance of those sport activities involving forward flexion of the trunk as well as when an additional weight was held anterior to the body.

Electromyographic studies by Wheatley and Jahnke have demonstrated that the hamstrings are strong thigh extensors while the gluteus maximus is active as an extensor only during strong resistance. In a study in progress involving the comparative magnitude of action potentials in the gluteus maximus, Houtz found that the greatest activity occurs when the subject contracts the muscles forcefully enough to decrease the inclination of the pelvic ring.* The sacrospinalis acting synergistically with the hamstrings supports the pelvis and gives added extension to the thigh by increasing the incline of the pelvic angle. This may be the reason that in the majority of sport activities herein reported activity in the gluteus maximus was found to be relatively minor.

The superficial thigh muscles during flexion, extension, and abduction and adduction of the erect subject were studied by Wheatley and Jahnke; during postural sway, by Joseph and Nightingale (1954); and during a variety of changes of one or more segments of the body by Houtz (1964). Results indicate that in addition to the primary action of the thigh muscles, they undoubtedly function from their attachment on the leg to overcome or modify the momentum initiated in the trunk, shoulder girdle, and upper extremities. The results of these investigations for a given activity were essentially the same and comparable to the findings in this study.

Previous studies by Houtz (1959, 1961) have demonstrated that changes in the position of one or more segments of the body causing total

realignment result in variations of muscle action patterns in the lower extremity. In the upright posture, muscles of the leg acting from their attachment on the foot alter or maintain the relationship of the leg to the foot. As the leg position is altered, a chain or kinetic reaction occurs at the knee and hip to adjust the segments above. Since a change in angle of the leg at the ankle changes the relationship of the line of gravity of the total body to the center of the base, either the original angle is re-established immediately or an adjustment of some body segment is autonomously made to again center the line of gravity over the base. Any change in the position of a body segment shifts the center of gravity within the body and other autonomous adjustments are made to balance the weight of the moving segment and recenter the line of gravity over the supporting base. During the swinging phase of a step, as the body weight moves forward, the tibialis anterior and long toe extensors pull the leg anteriorly over the foot. The phase of activity in the gastrocnemius occurs as the weight of the contralateral extremity swings through. During standing, contraction of the soleus moves the leg posteriorly, which tends to extend the knee, but the synergistic action of the gastrocnemius on the lower thigh maintains a slight degree of knee flexion. With the exception of the left gastrocnemius, action of the leg muscles in the present study is similar to that reported in previous publications. Apparently during the performance of one of the sport skills with electrodes on the left gastrocnemius, these were dislodged from contact with the skin surface. Thus, with the exception of bowling, volleyball spike, and basketball lay-up, the pattern of activity in the left gastrocnemius during the sport skills cannot be analyzed.

---

*In normal standing, the anterosuperior spine of the pelvis and the symphysis pubis are in approximately the same vertical plane. If the pelvic incline is decreased (backward tilt), the superior portion of the pelvis approaches a more horizontal position, the lumbar curve decreases, and the hips slightly extend. If the pelvic incline is increased (forward tilt), the superior portion approaches a more vertical position, the lumbar curve increases, and the hips slightly flex.

Chapter III

Methods and Procedures

THE subject for this study was a 30-year-old instructor of physical education. She is proficient in sport activities and she had participated previously in a series of studies in which these same skills (with the exception of bowling and golf) were studied photographically. In both bowling and golf, her skill is of tournament caliber.

Surface electrodes were used to obtain action potentials which, after appropriate amplification, were recorded on a multi-channel ink-writer Offner dynograph. Palpation during manual muscle testing by an experienced research physical therapist* was used to located the muscles studied. Silver disc surface electrodes, 0.8 cm in diameter, were placed over the belly of the muscle with a minimum interelectrode space of 2 to 3 cm. As a control to prevent variations which might influence the magnitude of the pen excursions in response to electrical activity, the distance between the paired electrodes and their placement on a muscle and the same muscle on the contralateral side were kept as constant as possible. The skin was cleansed and a mild erythema was produced by rubbing a selected area with electrode paste. The discs were filled with this substance and sealed in place with aeroplast and adhesive tape. To avoid as much as possible a pull on the electrodes during activity, the wires were looped and taped to the skin a few inches from the electrodes.

*This therapist has taught electrical diagnosis and worked extensively testing muscles of normal and pathological subjects (Groff and Houtz).

The following muscles were studied: gluteus maximus; gracilis; soleus; gastrocnemius; peroneus longus; extensor digitorum longus; tibialis anterior; tensor fasciae latae; sartorius; rectus femoris; vastus medialis; vastus lateralis; external hamstrings; internal hamstrings; sacrospinalis (in the lumbar region); rectus abdominis; external obliques; serratus anterior; lateral latissimus dorsi; medial latissimus dorsi; upper, middle, and lower trapezius; sternocleidomastoid; anterior, middle, and posterior deltoid; clavicular and sternal portions of the pectoralis major; biceps; triceps; brachioradialis; wrist and finger flexors and wrist and finger extensors. Electrode placement is schematically illustrated (Fig. 1). In placing the forearm electrodes, no attempt was made to isolate the wrist and finger muscles because of the magnitude of the study and the anatomical smallness of these muscles. Studies of the action of these two groups of muscles during stressful activities indicate synergistic action of all. Electrode placement on the biceps and triceps included both the long and short heads of each muscle and thus increased magnitude of electrical activity may indicate movement of the upper or lower arm, depending on the relation of one segment to another.

Seven muscles were recorded at a time. This required the subject to perform the thirteen sport skills ten times (twice for each lower extremity, twice for the trunk, and twice for each upper extremity). Muscles of the right and left extremities were sampled on different days, but right and left trunk muscles were sampled at

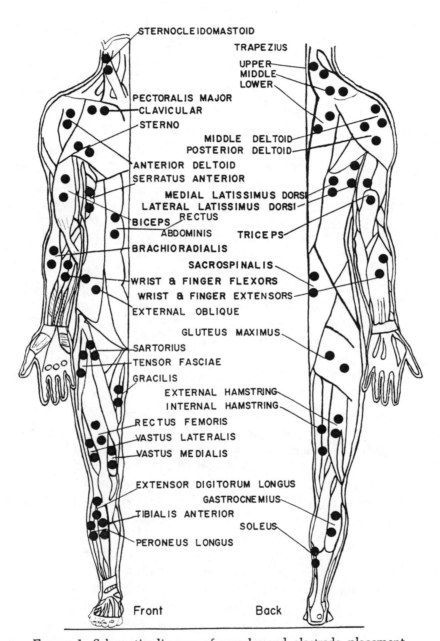

FIGURE 1. Schematic diagram of muscles and electrode placement.

the same time. To further verify the action of the trunk and shoulder girdle muscles during the various activities and to assist in coordinating trunk and upper extremity records, the entire series of skills was repeated an eleventh time with seven muscles in a different combination (three from the first set of seven trunk muscles tested, three from the second trunk set, and one from a right upper extremity group). The lateral latissimus dorsi muscles (right and left) were sampled in one of the trunk groups and also in an upper extremity group.

Prior to each recording session, the electromyograph was calibrated with the same setting of amplification for all channels and pen excursions were equalized. Because of the degree of electrical activity in the muscles of the right upper extremity in all activities, and the left upper extremity in bowling, it was necessary to set the microvolts at a lower gain. *Therefore, with the exception of bowling, the magnitude of the right and left upper extremity cannot be compared.* The magnitude of the microvolts is designated on each illustration. The speed of recording was 25 mm per second.

To check the accuracy of electrode placement on selected muscles and as an aid in interpreting the data, action potentials were recorded as the subject performed simple movements of flexion, extension, abduction, adduction, and rotation of various body segments. Electrical silence was recorded on the dynograph prior to the recording of each activity while the subject sat relaxed with feet resting on the floor. She then assumed the starting posture for the activity to be performed and, when the activity had been completed, she returned to a relaxed standing position. Electrical activity in the selected muscles was recorded throughout the procedure. The electrodes for a given set of muscles were undisturbed throughout the performance of the entire series of thirteen activities. Thus, the basic action patterns of muscles and the relative magnitude of electrical activity can be compared for the different activities.

An automatic wind Robot camera was used to photograph the subject during the performance of each skill. As the shutter of the camera was closed, a button was pressed to close the circuit, activating a magnetic signal suspended over the one channel of the electromyograph. This deflected the pen the instant the picture was taken. An attempt was made to take pictures during backswing, at contact, and during follow-through of each activity for each set of muscles. A number was placed in full view of the camera so that each picture could be matched with the correct record.

The study included the following skills: underhand throw, volleyball serve, badminton serve, bowling, golf (No. 5 iron), overhand throw, badminton clear, tennis serve, basketball throw (sidearm), tennis drive, batting, basketball lay-up, and volleyball spike. Insofar as possible, each skill was performed as in a game situation. Of necessity, all activities were performed in the laboratory, which may have modified the performance somewhat, particularly the force of delivery. The subject's field of operation was approximately twelve feet from the recording equipment. An operator held the terminal electrode box a few feet from the subject and moved with her as she performed each skill, thus minimizing the restrictive tendency of the wires. A 9 x 7 feet sheet was hung twenty feet from the area of release or contact to check the progress of the various balls and the badminton shuttle. Any modification in the performance of each specific skill is noted in the discussion of results. With the possible exception of the tennis serve, photographic comparisons of the subject's patterns of movement in this study with those in the previous work (Broer) indicated very few differences.

The subject was asked to perform the activity as she would normally. She was asked to concentrate on the activity and to disassociate herself from the operational details of the study. A team of five operators, each well-trained in the total procedure and in her specific duties, minimized operational instructions and problems.

Each activity was performed three or more times for each set of seven muscles. In all, 450 photographs (thirty to thirty-five for each activity) with matching electromyograms were obtained for analysis and comparison. In addition, 168 electromyograms were taken during simple movements to assist in the analysis of the more complicated skills.

The photographs were enlarged and used in the analysis of the movement patterns as portrayed by the muscle action. Each photograph was matched with its corresponding electromyogram. Using a Mimeoscope (opaque glass illuminated from below), three or more records of a set of muscles were superimposed and the patterns of electrical activity were compared. The points at which the various pictures were taken were combined on one record. Thus, the point of release or impact for a given skill could be determined for each group of muscles. This is illustrated by a line drawn through the illustration.

Since the electromyogram movement patterns were found to be highly repeatable, representative records were chosen for analysis. Muscles of the shoulder girdle and upper extremities were grouped together in one illustration, and the sacrospinalis, abdominals, and lower extremities were combined in another. Results are discussed for these two groupings separately and then summarized to give a picture of the total pattern.

When minor activity noted in the discussion cannot be seen in an illustration, it must be remembered that the electromyograms have been reduced considerably from the size of the original records. While activity, although minor, may have been clearly apparent on the original records which were used for analysis, reduction may cause it to be undiscernible in an illustration.

Since the wire attachments required a minimum of clothing during the electromyographic recording, the pictures taken at that time were not suitable for publication. So that pictures could be included in this monograph, 35 mm motion pictures were taken at a later date. A Bell and Howell Eyemo camera, which took forty-eight frames per second, was used. These films were viewed in a microfilm reader and frames were selected for printing. To give a clear picture of the movement sequence, some skills required more pictures than others.

Comparison of the three sequences of moving pictures taken of each skill indicated the same repeatability of movement that was seen in the electromyograms. When these pictures were compared to the still pictures taken during the electromyographic study, identical positions were seen. The movements during recording were the same as those shown in the pictures presented in this monograph except that the subject's reach may have been somewhat less in the tennis serve when performed in the laboratory.

The authors have attempted to portray the continuity of movement as well as suggest the activity of muscle patterns as they occur throughout given sport skills. It is unfortunate that the upper extremities and shoulder girdle records of necessity are separated from those of the trunk and lower extremities. To indicate the coordination of these segments, the action of the upper extremities and shoulder girdle is referred to in the analysis of the lower extremity movements.

Chapter IV

Underhand Pattern

SIMILARITIES of movement pattern in the underhand throw, volleyball serve, and badminton serve have been observed previously and recorded photographically by Broer (1960-1966). These observations appear to be substantiated by the electromyograms of muscular activity recorded during the performance of these activities. The underhand throw is analyzed in detail, but to avoid repetition the discussion of the volleyball and badminton serves is concentrated on the similarities and differences in magnitude and timing of the muscle patterns.

While the bowling movement may be considered an underhand pattern, the approach, the weight of the ball, and the stoop position at release are factors which cause differences in patterns of electrical activity. For this reason, bowling is discussed more fully than the volleyball and badminton serves, but again similarities to the throw are indicated.

UNDERHAND THROW

Shoulder Girdle and Upper Extremity Muscles

Preparatory Stance

Small amounts of electrical activity in selected muscles of the upper extremity and shoulder girdle are evident prior to the throw (extreme left of each column, Fig. 3, p. 14). Part of this action may have been preparatory and part caused by the position in which the subject stood. Both arms were held slightly in front of the body with the elbows flexed; both hands were on the ball (Fig. 2). Activity in the anterior deltoid and brachioradialis is evident. Bursts of activity in the clavicular portion of the left pectoralis muscle suggest that this shoulder was in forward flexion. The subject did stand with the ball toward the right side. The trunk was very slightly flexed at the hips. The head and shoulder girdle were carried erect and bi-lateral action of the middle and lower trapezius and latissimus dorsi muscles is apparent. Definite bursts of activity in the medial portion of the right latissimus dorsi suggest that a part of its action contributes to the stabilization of the trunk in preparation for action of the right upper extremity and shoulder girdle prior to the start of the backswing. Action of bilateral trapezius muscles apparently contributed to fixation of the scapulae for humeral action. Bursts of electrical activity in the left upper extremity and shoulder girdle muscles indicate the time that the left hand was removed from the ball.

The Throw

Release of the left hand and the start of the backswing of the right extremity is most obvious in the cessation of activity in the left brachioradialis and the clavicular portion of the left pectoralis. At this time, increased activity is seen in the right middle and posterior deltoid, triceps, and middle trapezius. These muscles probably contributed to retraction and fixation of the shoulder girdle and abduction and extension of the arm. The first bursts of activity in the right medial and possibly lateral portion of the latissimus dorsi precede slightly the activity in

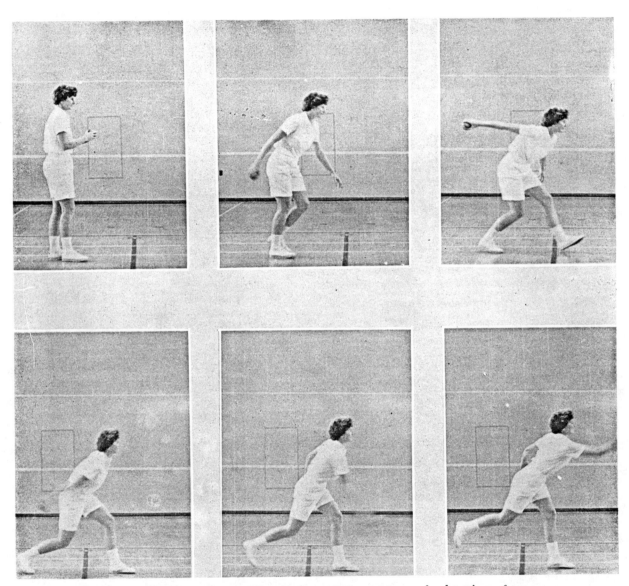

FIGURE 2. UNDERHAND THROW—Frames from motion pictures of subject's performance.

UNDERHAND THROW

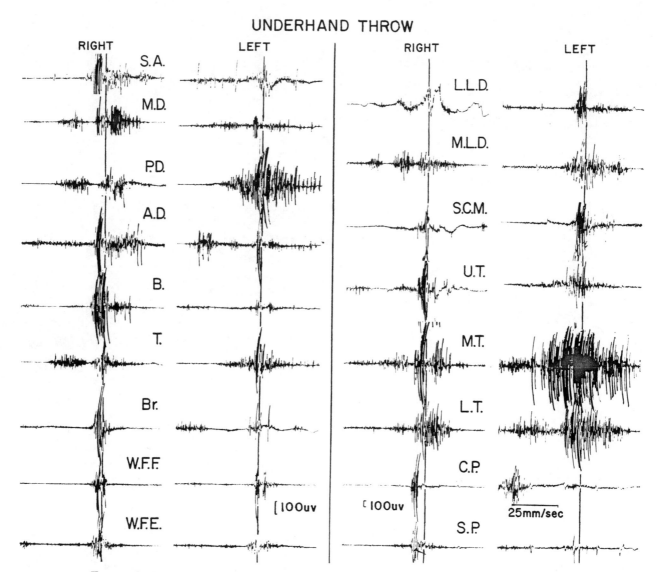

FIGURE 3. UNDERHAND THROW—Activity in muscles of shoulder girdle and upper extremity: serratus anterior (S.A.); middle (M.D.), posterior (P.D.), and anterior (A.D.) deltoid; biceps (B.); triceps (T.); brachioradialis (Br.); wrist and finger flexors (W.F.F.) and extensors (W.F.E.); lateral (L.L.D.) and medial (M.L.D.) latissimus dorsi; sternocleidomastoid (S.C.M.); upper (U.T.), middle (M.T.), and lower (L.T.) trapezius; clavicular (C.P.), and sternal (S.P.) pectoralis major. The vertical line through the electromyograms indicates the point of release.

the above muscles. This suggests that the latissimus dorsi was involved in initiating the backward swing of the right arm. Activity in this muscle ceases during the downward swing and through the center of the arc, the time when gravity is effective. A second burst of activity occurs apparently to help momentum and the other muscles effect maximum extension. During the backswing, variable magnitudes of activity are seen in most of the muscles of the right arm and shoulder as some directed the motion and others stabilized the shoulder and trunk. The lack of observable activity in the right wrist and finger flexors during the backswing is interesting.

At the top of the backswing of the right arm, a split second diminution of activity is seen in the right triceps, middle and posterior deltoid, medial portion of the latissimus dorsi, and middle and lower trapezius. Simultaneously, the right serratus anterior and biceps are seen to contract, apparently to brake the extensor action of the extremity and act in the initiating of the forward motion of the scapula and arm. Concurrent action of the anterior deltoid and pectoralis major muscles follows immediately. Then electrical activity in the rest of the right shoulder girdle and upper extremity muscles is seen to increase. The biceps may have been active in the maintenance of supination of the forearm while the triceps controlled the tendency of the biceps and brachioradialis to flex the forearm. Increased activity in the brachioradialis during the forward swing suggests that while the elbow was extended, this muscle may have prevented overextension by the triceps and thus been effective in the stabilization of the elbow. The electrical activity of the wrist and finger flexors and extensors increases in magnitude toward the end of the forward swing, crescendos during release, and the extensors continue some activity into the follow-through. It appears that these muscles acted synergistically to control the ball prior to release and the extensors decelerated wrist flexion following release. The right serratus anterior and anterior and middle deltoid muscles reach their peak and then diminish in

activity before the point of release. The posterior and middle deltoids burst in the follow-through, probably acting to brake the momentum of the right upper extremity.

After the left hand released the ball, as the right latissimus dorsi became active, activity is seen in the left anterior deltoid. Immediately after this, activity in the left anterior deltoid diminishes and the left triceps and posterior deltoid become active to maintain the left arm position as the shoulder girdle rotated to the right. As the right arm moved backward, the left was extended and held free of the body. Action is seen in the left triceps, posterior deltoid, and latissimus dorsi. It appears that the relatively small amount of rotation was largely shoulder girdle movement. Activity in the left middle and lower trapezius may have counteracted the pull of the right extremity caused by the motion of the backswing of the right arm reducing shoulder rotation to the right. The left triceps, posterior deltoid, latissimus dorsi, and brachioradialis crescendo during the time that the right arm was swinging forward and the left arm was being drawn back and flexed at the elbow. At release, bursts of activity in the muscles of the left extremity reflect the activity in the right.

The momentary increase of activity in the left anterior deltoid and serratus anterior in time with the right latissimus dorsi indicates a reciprocal action of the two extremities. In addition to acting on the arm, the right and left latissimus dorsi may have been active in preventing or minimizing trunk rotation and in assisting in trunk extension. Action potentials are seen in the right and left upper trapezius and sternocleidomastoid muscles, indicating that these muscles may have been active in maintaining the head in a forward position so that the subject could see the target.

Back, Abdominal, and Lower Extremity Muscles

Preparatory Stance

Action potentials are seen in the selected leg and thigh muscles as the preparatory stance was maintained (Fig. 4, p. 16). The subject

UNDERHAND THROW

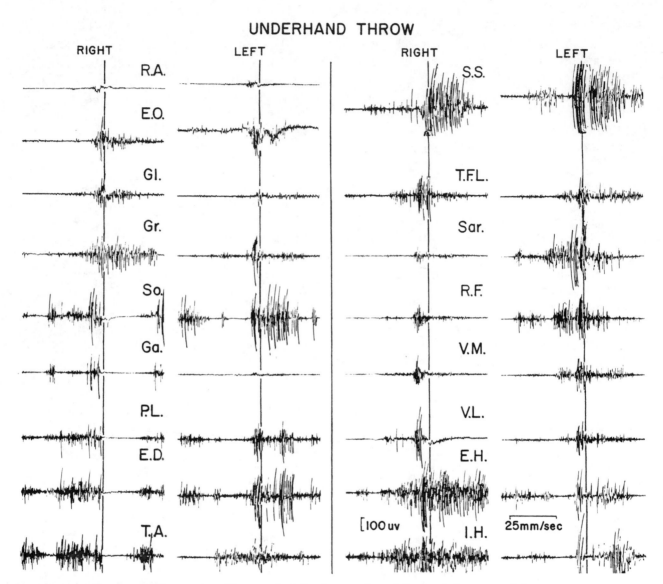

FIGURE 4. UNDERHAND THROW—Activity in muscles of back, abdomen, and lower extremity: rectus abdominis (R.A.); external oblique (E.O.); gluteus maximus (Gl); gracilis (Gr.); soleus (So.); gastrocnemius (Ga.); peroneus longus (P.L.); extensor digitorum longus (E.D.); tibialis anterior (T.A.) sacrospinalis (S.S.); tensor fasciae latae (T.F.L.); sartorius (Sar.); rectus femoris (R.F.); vastus medialis (V.M.), and lateralis (V.L.); external (E.H.) and internal (I.H.) hamstrings. The vertical line through the electromyograms indicates the point of release.

stood with her feet comfortably apart and with slightly more weight on the left foot. The bilateral soleus (more left), peroneus longus, toe extensors, and the right tibialis anterior, acting from their attachments on the feet, were involved in stabilizing the legs and maintaining dorsiflexion at the ankles. The lack of activity in the left tibialis anterior and the considerable activity of the soleus are indicative of the fact that the subject carried slightly more weight on this foot in preparation for the push onto the right foot. Bilateral activity in the hamstrings probably contributed to the maintenance of the very slight degree of flexion at the hips and to stabilization of the knee. Slight activity in the sacrospinalis and external oblique muscles is undoubtedly indicative of their involvement in the stabilization of the trunk and, with the shoulder muscles, in the maintenance of trunk extension.

The Throw

Immediately before the beginning of the backswing of the upper right extremity, the right foot was lifted to start the transference of weight backward. The weight on the left foot is evident in the bursts of electrical activity in the left sartorius, rectus femoris, and continued activity in the soleus, peroneus longus, and toe extensors. Lifting the right foot in order to step backward is seen in the activity in the hamstrings (knee flexors) and in the bursts of activity in the right soleus and gastrocnemius (plantar flexors) concurrent with diminution of activity in the right tibialis anterior and toe extensors. Immediately thereafter, action potentials increase in the right peroneus longus, toe extensors, tibialis anterior, tensor fasciae latae, hamstrings, and slightly in the quadriceps, while the soleus, and to a lesser degree gastrocnemius, continue to be active. These muscles were actively involved in the balancing of most of the body weight on the right foot.

During the backswing, activity is seen in the left sartorius, rectus femoris and vastus medialis. The subject stepped through with the left extremity, extending the knee and dorsiflexing

the foot so that the heel touched the floor first. The latter is evidenced by activity in the left extensor digitorum longus and tibialis anterior. Because of the forward-backward stride position, the pelvis was rotated somewhat to the right with a resultant inward rotation of the right and outward rotation of the left thigh. This may have been assisted by activity in the right gracilis and left sartorius. More activity is apparent in the right sacrospinalis at the initiation of the transference of weight to the right foot, and then the activity of the left increases, probably to contribute to fixation of the trunk during the backswing and thus prevent considerable trunk rotation or bend to the right.

Reversal of the upper extremity from backswing to forward swing was preceded by the beginning of the shift in weight from the right to left foot. Increased potentials are seen in the right tensor fasciae latae, sartorius, quadriceps, hamstrings, gluteus maximus, gracilis, soleus, gastrocnemius, peroneus longus, toe extensors, and anterior tibialis muscles as the weight was transferred forward.

As the weight was taken on the left lower extremity, activity is seen to increase in all leg and thigh muscles of this limb, although that in the gastrocnemius* and gluteus maximus is very slight. The increased activity in the tensor fasciae latae, gracilis, sartorius, and quadriceps suggests that they were stabilizing the flexing hip and knee and modifying the rotary forces acting on the pelvis. The hamstrings were probably contributing to hip stabilization while the soleus, gastrocnemius, peroneus longus, toe extensors, and tibialis anterior, acting from their attachment on the foot, balanced the leg over the foot.

Minor activity is seen in the left external oblique during the backswing. During the forward swing, the right and left external obliques, rectus abdominis (left more than right), and sacrospinalis (left considerably more than right) are active. The abdominal muscles may have acted to stabilize the rib cage and pelvis, and,

---

*Left gastrocnemius electrodes apparently had been loosened (see explanation, p. 7).

with the sacrospinalis, may have modified trunk rotation.

As the ball was released, electrical potentials from the muscles of the right lower leg diminish to almost nothing. This subject lifted her extended right leg and held it off the ground on the follow-through phase of the throw. Increased activity at release is obvious in the right sacrospinalis, which undoubtedly, with the left sacrospinalis, contributed to the support of the trunk in a somewhat forward-flexed position during follow-through. Both the right and left oblique muscles continue to show some activity during follow-through. The supporting of the weight by the left extremity is seen in the bursts of activity in the hamstrings, peroneus longus, and toe extensors and continued activity in the left lower extremity muscles. The erect posture was finally assumed and balance between the extremities is evidenced by the resumption of activity potentials in the muscles of the right lower leg (soleus, gastrocnemius, peroneus longus, extensor digitorum longus, and tibialis anterior).

VOLLEYBALL SERVE (UNDERHAND)

Shoulder Girdle and Upper Extremity Muscles

Preparatory Stance

The electrical activity in the upper extremities and shoulder girdle prior to the beginning of the backswing is evident in the same muscles as for the underhand throw (Fig. 6, p. 20). The right medial latissimus dorsi and the clavicular portion of the left pectoralis major were slightly less active as the subject prepared for the serve than for the throw. The left biceps and wrist and finger flexors and extensors were slightly more active as they acted on the forearm and hand to support the ball. The left lower trapezius was slightly more active in the serve, possibly to stabilize the shoulder girdle of the extremity holding the ball.

The Serve

The timing and magnitude of muscular activity of the right arm and shoulder girdle during the serve closely approximates that seen during the throw. The beginning of the backswing is indicated by increased activity in the right posterior deltoid and triceps which is followed immediately by increased activity in the middle deltoid, middle trapezius, and medial latissimus dorsi. Activity in the latter three may occur very slightly later in the serve than appears to be the case in the throw. As in the throw, the first increase in the activity of both sections of the latissimus dorsi slightly precedes that of the deltoid and triceps and, therefore, again there is the suggestion that this muscle was involved in the initiation of the backswing of the right arm. The same pattern of reduced activity through the center of the backward arc and a renewed burst of activity in this muscle during the last part of the backswing is apparent in both the serve and the throw. Considerably more activity is seen in the right lateral latissimus dorsi during the backswing of the serve than the throw. This may indicate more control of the serve backswing, or it may be that even the apparently negligible weight of the ball involved in the throw is effective in increasing the momentum of the arm because of being held at the end of the long lever. Other than this, and very slight activity in the wrist and finger flexors as the subject made a fist during the volleyball serve, the muscular activity during the backswing appears to be comparable to that of the throw.

As in the throw, the top of the backswing of the right arm is marked by a short diminution or cessation of activity in the right triceps, middle and posterior deltoid, medial portion of the latissimus dorsi, and middle and lower trapezius. The simultaneous contraction of the right serratus anterior and biceps is again apparent, and activity in the anterior deltoid and pectoralis muscles follows immediately. Electrical activity in the rest of the muscles of the right arm and shoulder then increases. This pattern is the same as that of the underhand throw, except that in the volleyball serve the activity in the biceps momentarily diminishes immedi-

FIGURE 5. VOLLEYBALL SERVE—Frames from motion pictures of subject's performance.

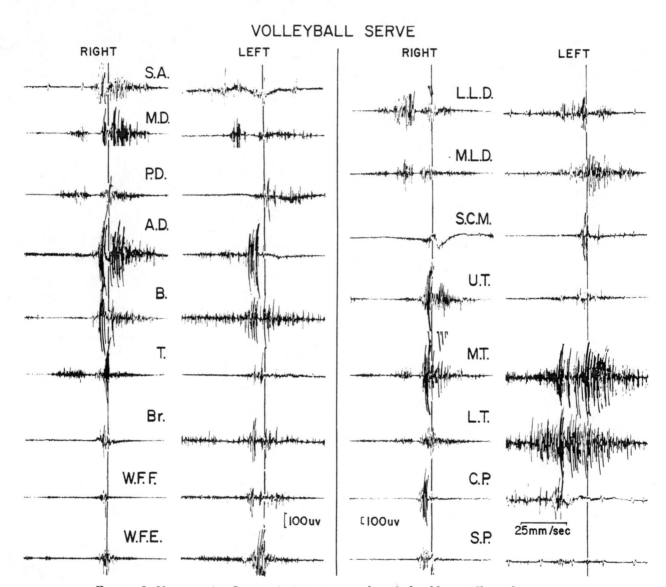

FIGURE 6. VOLLEYBALL SERVE—Activity in muscles of shoulder girdle and upper extremity. See Figure 3 for muscle symbols. Note similarity of timing and pattern of activity in right muscles of Figures 3 and 6.

ately before contact. This coincides with a like diminution of activity in the anterior deltoid which is evident in the records for both throw and the serve. Activity in the triceps at contact appears greater in the serve than in the throw and that in the brachioradialis and wrist and finger flexors and extensors appears to be less in the records of the serve. This raises the question as to whether the elbow may participate forcefully with the wrist in giving the final impetus in throwing the ball while both must be stabilized to withstand the force of impact of the strike. Apparently less activity was required to stabilize the wrist for impact (serve) than for use of the wrist in giving the final impetus to the ball (throw) and then to act as a brake for the flexion.

The greatest difference in timing and magnitude of electrical activity during the throw and serve is apparent in the left arm records and was caused by the toss of the ball. This extremity performed a directly purposive movement in the serve, but in the throw it did not. Since the ball was held in the left hand and tossed, cessation or decrease of activity in the left anterior deltoid, brachioradialis, and clavicular portion of the pectoralis muscles is apparent in the throw record at the time the left hand was withdrawn from the ball prior to the throw, but is not seen on the serve record. Bursts of activity in the middle and lower trapezius in time with the pectoralis major (particularly the clavicular portion) and the serratus anterior indicate that the left shoulder and arm were moved forward across the body so that the ball was positioned for the hit by the right hand, and bursts of sequential activity in the anterior deltoid and biceps, followed immediately by brachioradialis and wrist and finger flexors signal the toss of the ball.

The left posterior deltoid is considerably more active throughout the throw and follow-through than the serve, although a similar pattern of activity is apparent during the follow-through of both skills. Both the left biceps and brachioradialis show more activity during the serve than the throw. Although the left middle trapezius is very active in both activities, and essentially the same timing is apparent, the activity appears greater in the throw. This is also true of the left upper trapezius and sternocleidomastoid.

Back, Abdominal, and Lower Extremity Muscles

The pattern of activity seen in the back, abdominal, and lower extremity muscles during the performance of the volleyball serve and the underhand throw is almost identical.

Preparatory Stance

The only differences in the muscular activity during the preparation for the serve and the throw are seen in the lack of activity in the right tibialis anterior and reduced activity in the right toe extensors on the serve record (Fig. 7, p. 22). Apparently the subject's weight was more evenly distributed (not as much forward on the left foot) as she prepared for the serve, or she may have been more relaxed.

The Serve

Immediately before the beginning of the backswing of the right upper extremity, the weight was shifted to the left foot, as evidenced by bursts of activity in the right tibialis anterior and toe extensors concurrent with activity in the left sartorius, rectus femoris, and continued activity in the left soleus, peroneus longus, and toe extensors. The right foot then appears to have been immediately moved backward as in the throw, although it seems to have been moved less, since the diminution of activity in the right tibialis anterior appears to be of slightly shorter duration and the bursts of activity in the right gastrocnemius and soleus are less pronounced than in the throw record.

As the subject balanced her weight on the right foot, the pattern of electrical activity seen in the records of the muscles of the right lower extremity is the same as for the throw. Action potentials increase in the right peroneus longus, toe extensors, tibialis anterior, tensor fasciae latae, hamstrings, and again only slightly in the quadriceps, while the soleus, and to a lesser

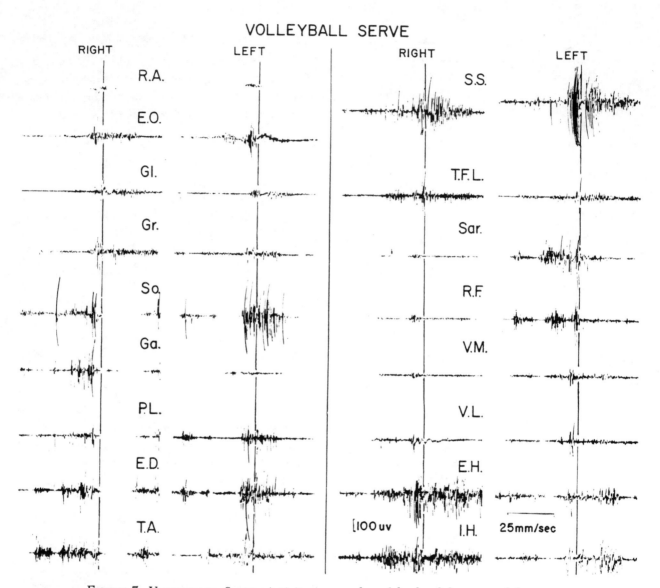

FIGURE 7. VOLLEYBALL SERVE—Activity in muscles of back, abdomen, and lower extremity. See Figure 4 for muscle symbols. Although the magnitude of electrical activity is less during the volleyball serve than the throw, the timing and pattern during these two activities are nearly identical (Figs. 7 and 4).

degree the gastrocnemius, continue to show activity.

During the backswing, the muscular activity of the lower extremities is almost identical to that found for the throw. The activity in the abdominals and sacrospinalis muscles is also very similar. There may be slightly less activity in the left sacrospinalis.

As in the throw, the shift of weight from the right to the left foot for the serve is seen in increased potentials in the right tensor fasciae latae, sartorius, quadriceps, hamstrings, gluteus maximus, gracilis, soleus, gastrocnemius, peroneus longus, toe extensors, and tibialis anterior. While the timing is identical to that of the throw, the magnitude of the potentials in these muscles during the serve is less than in the throw, except for that in the gastrocnemius, which is greater.

As the weight was taken on the left foot, increased activity is seen in all left leg and thigh muscles, although that of the gluteus maximus and gastrocnemius* is again, as in the throw, slight.

Activity in the right soleus and gastrocnemius diminishes immediately prior to contact. This change may be very slightly earlier than in the throw. At contact, as on release of the ball in the throw, the activity in all right lower leg muscles diminishes as the subject lifted her right leg off the ground. During the follow-through, the electrical activity in the supporting left extremity, lifted right extremity, abdominal and sacrospinalis muscles is identical for the two skills. The magnitude of activity potential is slightly greater in the underhand throw, possibly indicating that a greater effort was needed to brake the forward momentum resulting from the throw.

———

*Left gastrocnemius electrode apparently had been loosened (see explanation, p. 7).

BADMINTON SERVE

Shoulder Girdle and Upper Extremity Muscles

Preparatory Stance

As the subject prepared to serve the shuttle cock, activity is seen again in the same muscles as for the underhand throw and the volleyball serve (Fig. 9, p. 25). The activity appears to have been less in all three sections of the right trapezius, the middle and lower sections of the left trapezius, the medial portion of the latissimus dorsi, the left clavicular portion of the pectoralis major, and the wrist and finger extensors. Greater activity is seen in the brachioradialis and the wrist and finger flexors as the racket was grasped.

The Serve

In general, the pattern of muscular activity in the right arm and shoulder girdle is identical to that for the underhand throw and the volleyball serve. As would be anticipated, the wrist and finger flexors are more active during the forward swing and impact of the badminton serve than of the volleyball serve and somewhat more active than in the throw. A comparison of these muscles in the throw and badminton serve shows a break at release of the ball, but continued activity as the racket hit the shuttlecock. The biphasic activity of the wrist and finger extensors indicates the different wrist movement in the badminton serve from that in the other two skills.

Somewhat less activity is seen in the lower trapezius during the badminton serve than the throw, but the former is very similar to that in the volleyball serve. The activity pattern for the right medial latissimus dorsi differs for the badminton serve. The burst of activity during the backswing appears to be greater than for either of the other two activities and coincides with a small burst in the upper trapezius which is not apparent on the other two records.

As was found when comparing the volleyball serve to the throw, the greatest difference in muscle function during the badminton serve and the underhand throw is found in the left shoulder and upper extremity. As would be anticipated, the pattern of activity in this extremity during the badminton serve more close-

FIGURE 8. BADMINTON SERVE—Frames from motion pictures of subject's performance.

BADMINTON SERVE

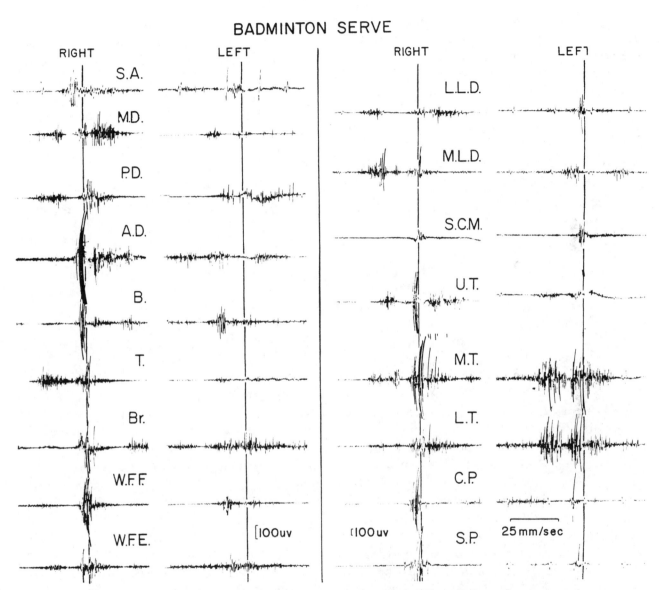

FIGURE 9. BADMINTON SERVE—Activity in muscles of shoulder girdle and upper extremity. See Figure 3 for muscle symbols. The timing and pattern of the right extremity and shoulder girdle are very similar to those of Figures 3 and 6.

ly approximates that of the volleyball serve than the underhand throw. However, the degree of activity is considerably less. The bursts of activity in the left middle deltoid and biceps, followed immediately by the clavicular portion and then the sternal portion of the pectoralis major, signal the release of the shuttle. It is interesting to note that in the volleyball serve in which the ball was tossed, the bursts of activity in the clavicular portion of the pectoralis major precede bursts in the middle deltoid, biceps, and wrist and finger muscles, while in badminton, in which the shuttle was dropped, these muscles burst simultaneously and are followed by the pectoralis major.

Back, Abdominal, and Lower Extremity Muscles

The muscular activity in the back, abdominal, and lower extremity muscles was considerably less during the performance of the badminton serve than either the underhand throw or volleyball serve (Fig. 10, p. 27). This could be expected since this skill involves a light racket which lengthens the lever but is light enough to be manipulated very rapidly by the smaller muscles, and a light shuttlecock which does not produce a great deal of force to be resisted at impact. Thus, through speed, considerable force (sufficient for this purpose) can be produced by the upper extremity with a minimum of trunk and lower extremity action. The timing of the activity in the abdominal and right extremity muscles, with the exception of the gastrocnemius and hamstrings during follow-through, is the same as during the underhand throw and volleyball serve. There are more differences in the left leg function, but in general the bursts of activity which are seen in the badminton serve coincide with bursts in the underhand throw.

Preparatory Stance

The outstanding difference in the preparatory stance is obvious in the lack of activity in the left soleus, peroneus longus, and toe extensors as the subject prepared to hit the shuttle as compared to the bursts of activity in these muscles

before the throw and the volleyball serve (Figs. 4,7,10).

The Serve

The indications of an active backward weight transference, which are obvious in the records of the throw and volleyball serve, are not seen in the badminton serve record. The early bursts of activity in the right tibialis anterior, toe extensors, and soleus may indicate resistance to the tendency to move the weight backward at the beginning of the stroke.

As in the throw and volleyball serve, some activity, although negligible in the sartorius, rectus femoris, and vastus medialis, is seen in all muscles of the right thigh and leg during the backswing. Evidence of stabilization of the right extremity is seen in the right tensor fasciae latae, hamstrings, peroneus longus, tibialis anterior, and toe extensors, which were active throughout. Activity in the soleus and gastrocnemius increased markedly toward the top of the backswing and beginning of the forward swing indicating the reversal of the direction of movement. This pattern is also seen in the throw and serve, although the bursts in the soleus and gastrocnemius appear to be slightly earlier in the badminton serve. The comparatively little activity in the left lower extremity muscles during the backswing may indicate that any movement of weight backward onto the right foot took place as a result of the movement of the upper extremity rather than active pushing of the weight backward by the left leg. The left hamstrings, and to a lesser degree the soleus, were active at the end.

On the forward swing, similarities of pattern are seen in the right soleus, gastrocnemius, gluteus maximus, and gracilis. Bursts of activity occur in the first two muscles, followed immediately by increased activity in the second two. The magnitude of potentials is greatest in the underhand throw, less in the volleyball serve, and least in the badminton serve. Activity in the soleus and gastrocnemius decreases markedly, and seemingly ceases immediately before impact. This pattern is also seen in the soleus

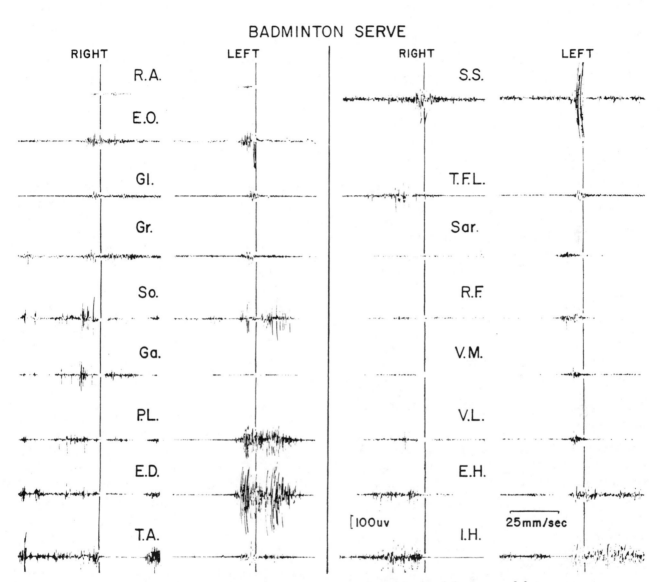

BADMINTON SERVE

FIGURE 10. BADMINTON SERVE—Activity in muscles of back, abdomen, and lower extremity. See Figure 4 for muscle symbols. Thigh muscles are less active than during performance of previous two activities. However, considerable similarity of leg muscle activity is seen in Figures 4, 7, and 10.

during the throw and the volleyball serve, although the magnitude of activity is less for badminton. The activity in the gluteus maximus does decrease at release (throw) and contact (volleyball), but since the magnitude is greater, it does not appear to cease at that time. Activity in the right tensor fasciae latae diminishes rather than increases as it does in the throw and volleyball serve. The right hamstrings fade out by contact, the weight having been taken by the left extremity but the right toes being kept on the floor, while in the throw and volleyball serve they continue to be extremely active. The taking of additional weight by the left extremity is seen in bursts of activity in all muscles except the gastrocnemius.*

Activity of the abdominal and sacrospinalis muscles shows the same pattern during the back and forward swing of the badminton serve as during the throw and volleyball serve, although again the muscles were less active.

During follow-through, the differences in muscular activity in the badminton serve reflect differences in posture and movement. In the throw and volleyball serve, this subject extended her right hip, raising this extremity off the floor with the trunk well forward, while in the badminton serve the right knee was relaxed and the toes remained on the floor. This difference is most obvious in the lack of activity in the right hamstrings as compared to the extensive activity during the follow-through of both the throw and the volley-ball serve. Less activity is also seen in the sacrospinalis muscles since, in the throw and volleyball serve, these muscles were involved in supporting the trunk which was more forward than in the badminton serve.

---

*Left gastrocnemius electrode apparently had been loosened (see explanation, p. 7).

BOWLING

In order to reduce friction during the slide, the subject removed her left tennis shoe, leaving on a cotton sock.

Shoulder Girdle and Upper Extremity Muscles

Preparatory Stance

Bilateral action in the anterior deltoid and pectoral muscles occurred to hold the arms in front of the body (Fig. 12, p. 30). Activity in the right and left biceps and brachioradialis flexed the elbows and with the wrist and finger flexors and extensors supported the weight of the ball. The magnitude of electrical activity in most of the left muscles, being greater than the right,* suggests that the ball was held toward the right side and that the left extremity carried the greater burden in supporting the heavy ball.

All muscles of the shoulder girdle were active to stabilize the shoulder girdle against the anteriorly imposed load and to maintain the more

---

*In bowling, the microvolts were the same for the right and left arms and, therefore, the magnitude of activity can be compared.

or less erect trunk position. Action in the two upper trapezius muscles contributed both to holding the head erect and resisting the downward pull on the shoulder girdle due to the weight of the ball. The magnitude of electrical activity in this muscle is comparable in the two extremities.

The Throw

As the ball was pushed forward over the right lower extremity, activity increased in the bilateral anterior deltoid and clavicular portion of the pectoralis major muscles. The biceps may have contributed to the forward flexion of the arms as well as acting with the brachioradialis to control the gravitational forces extending the elbow. As the upper extremities moved toward the forward position, approximately chest high, a gradual increase in activity is seen in the bilateral serratus anterior and middle and lower trapezius muscles to stabilize the shoulder girdle and counteract the downward pull of gravity. Greater activity apparently was required in the left lower trapezius to aid in keeping the shoul-

FIGURE 11. BOWLING—Frames from motion pictures of subject's performance.

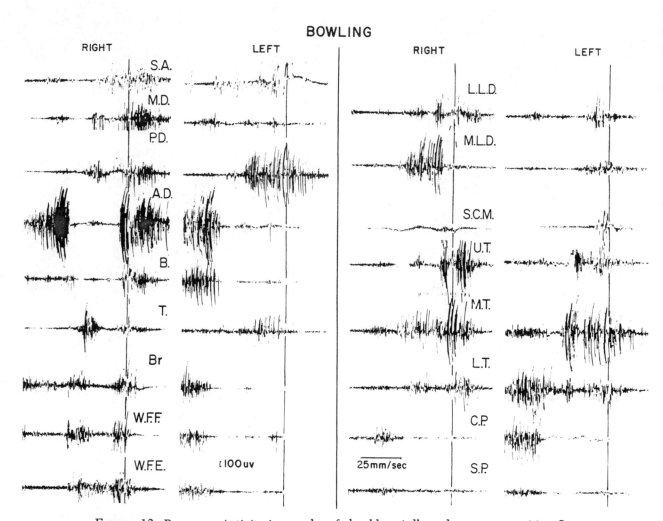

FIGURE 12. BOWLING—Activity in muscles of shoulder girdle and upper extremities. See Figure 3 for muscle symbols. Note that this is the only activity for which the "uv" was the same for right and left upper extremities.

der girdle level. The middle deltoids also show some increase in activity, as does the left latissimus dorsi, probably to direct the motion of the arm. The wrist and finger muscles continued to act to support and maintain the grip on the ball.

Beginning of the backswing is most obvious in the cessation of activity in the left brachioradialis and wrist and finger flexors and extensors as this hand was removed from the ball. With release of the left hand, activity increases in the right brachioradialis, and the wrist and finger flexors and extensors as the right extremity took the complete weight of the ball. A cessation or diminution of electrical activity in the left anterior and middle deltoid, biceps, and pectoralis major muscles follows immediately.

The right pectoralis major, anterior and middle deltoid, and biceps muscles continue to be active, probably having been involved in guiding the beginning of the swing, and then they also cease as gravity was allowed to effect the swing. At this time, activity increases in the right triceps, latissimus dorsi, middle trapezius and then the lower trapezius and middle and posterior deltoid to retract the shoulder girdle and upper extremity as the ball moved upward toward the top of the backswing. Minor amounts of activity occur in the right serratus anterior during the backswing, increasing toward the end, probably to stabilize the scapula, to check the retraction of the shoulder girdle, and then to start the forward swing.

As the right extremity moved through the backswing, the left was held in abduction with the elbow extended by action of the posterior deltoid and triceps. These muscles were more active as abductors because of the flexed position of the trunk. The left middle and lower trapezius and latissimus dorsi acting with the contralateral muscles may have assisted in maintaining the shoulders facing the target and the upper trapezius in extending the head on a forward-flexed trunk.

The beginning of the forward swing is indicated by diminution of activity in the right latissimus dorsi as it ceased to extend the arm and by increased activity in the right upper trape-

zius as it burst to hold the shoulder girdle for reversal of direction and downward movement of the arm. Simultaneously, activity occurs in the brachioradialis and wrist and finger flexors and extensors to control the ball. Immediately thereafter, activity in the anterior deltoid and biceps increases to forward flex the arm as the middle, and to a lesser degree the posterior, deltoid probably were guiding it. Activity in the right middle trapezius, serratus anterior, and to a lesser degree the lower portion of the trapezius, indicates that these muscles functioned to stabilize the shoulder.

The muscles of the left extremity, which are active during the backswing, continue to be active during the forward swing and into follow-through. Minor action potentials are seen also in the wrist and finger flexors and extensor muscles. These may be reflex in nature. Bursts of activity in the left sternocleidomastoid may have stabilized the head while the right upper trapezius acted on the shoulder girdle.

As the ball was released, an instantaneous pause in the electrical activity of the right anterior deltoid occurs. Perhaps the momentum of the heavy ball was so great that this muscle relaxed to avoid interfering with the movement. After the split-second pause, the anterior deltoid bursts again and with the other portions of this muscle and the biceps, it continued to forward flex the arm in the follow-through phase. The triceps, with gravity, maintained the semi-extended elbow. The brachioradialis and wrist and finger flexors burst at release and taper off early in the follow-through phase while the wrist and finger extensor action continues longer. The right serratus anterior and middle trapezius muscles show relatively little change in activity at release as they continued to support the shoulder girdle into the follow-through phase. The upper and lower portions of the trapezius joined in this action immediately after release. Diminution of action potentials of all muscles active in the follow-through phase indicate a return of the erect posture.

While in bowling the weight of the ball caused a considerably greater magnitude of electrical activity during the preparatory stance, the pattern of activity during the swing is similar in many ways to that for the underhand throw.

The pattern of activity in the right middle and posterior deltoid and middle trapezius muscles is the same for the two skills. The activity in the right anterior deltoid is the same, except that the very great activity seen as the ball was held and pushed away is not seen in the throw record, and the activity of this muscle was less during the throw follow-through. The triceps pattern is the same; however, the magnitude is greater during the bowling backswing and throw release. It is interesting to note that the activity in the right biceps and brachioradialis muscles is considerably less during the bowling forward swing and release, while these muscles show greater activity during the first part of the bowling backswing, again because of the heavier ball. The pattern of activity in the right medial latissimus dorsi differs for the two activities as does that of the pectoralis major.

While it appears that in general the left arm was more active in the throw than in bowling, this cannot be concluded since bowling was the only activity for which the microvolts for the left arm were set equal to the right arm. However, where the activity appears greater for bowling, as seen in the preparatory position when the left hand supported the heavy ball, the difference has meaning. The burst of activity in the left anterior deltoid, brachioradialis, and wrist and finger extensors at release of the throw is not seen on the bowling record.

Back, Abdominal, and Lower Extremity Muscles
Preparatory Stance

Action in the bilateral sacrospinalis and hamstrings* contributed to maintenance of the starting position with the weight held in front of the body (Fig. 13). The degree of electrical activity in the left sacrospinalis may have counteracted the weight of the ball being carried

---

*The electrodes on the right internal hamstrings were apparently dislodged as the subject took her first approach and no record was obtained.

toward the right side. A comparison of the activity in the right and left soleus, peroneus longus, toe extensors, and the minor activity in the left thigh muscles and tibialis anterior suggests that more weight may have been carried on this extremity.

The Approach

The first step is evidenced by increased activity in the right tibialis anterior as the leg was pulled over the foot and the ankle maintained in slight dorsiflexion during the swing phase and at heel strike. Simultaneous activity occurs in the right gracilis followed immediately by bursts of activity in the quadriceps and tensor fasciae latae to flex the extremity. In the supporting left extremity, increased activity occurs mainly in the left hamstrings, while the soleus, peroneus longus, and toe extensors continue to show great activity and lesser degrees of activity (only a trace in some) are seen in the quadriceps, tensor fasciae latae, gracilis, and tibialis anterior.

The stance phase of the right extremity is evident in decreased activity in the right anterior tibialis and increased electrical activity in the other muscles of this leg (soleus, gastrocnemius, peroneus longus, and toe extensors). Since the subject was in a semi-crouch position, activity also occurs in the gracilis, gluteus maximus, tensor fasciae latae, hamstrings, and to a slight degree the quadriceps. At the same time, activity in the left tibialis anterior, rectus femoris, and sartorius started this extremity in the swing phase. The peroneus longus and toe extensors also contributed to this motion.

The beginning of the next step by the right is evidenced by bursts of activity in the right tibialis anterior, tensor fasciae latae, sartorius, rectus femoris, and vastus medialis and diminution in activity in the hamstrings, gluteus maximus, gracilis, soleus, gastrocnemius, and peroneus longus. Those muscles which show a diminution of activity in the right extremity show bursts of activity in the left as the weight was being carried on this extremity.

After the weight was transferred to the right,

BOWLING

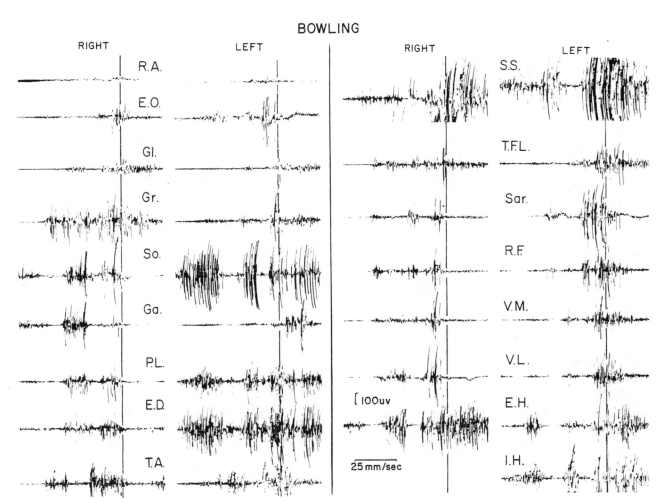

FIGURE 13. BOWLING—Activity in muscles of back, abdomen, and lower extremity. See Figure 4 for muscle symbols. The stance and swing phase of the leg muscles is much like that seen in walking. Much more activity is seen in the thigh muscles because of the semi-crouch position.

it was shifted back onto the left extremity as the subject went into the slide prior to release of the ball. This is evident in the pattern of activity in the left leg. There is a burst in the left tibialis anterior, simultaneous with a diminution of activity in the soleus, peroneus longus, and toe extensors. This is followed immediately by a diminution in tibialis anterior activity and a renewed burst in the other three muscles. As the weight was taken on the left flexed extremity, there is increased or continued activity in all thigh muscles. In the interim, the right extremity was flexed at the hip and knee and dorsiflexed at the ankle. It was gradually extended until immediately before release when it was lifted from the floor with the hip almost completely extended. Action of the right hamstrings, tensor fasciae latae, gluteus maximus, and gracilis is seen during the follow-through phase. Activity diminishes as the subject assumed the erect posture.

Activity in the sacrospinalis maintained the shoulder girdle and trunk in a position facing the target and resisted gravitational forces tending to further flex the trunk. During the forward swing, there was a tendency for the body to follow the ball, and the strong contraction seen in the left sacrospinalis and probably the external oblique may have prevented this movement. The increase and decrease in magnitude of electrical activity in the sacrospinalis in time with activity in the thigh and leg muscles suggest that they act to stabilize the pelvis. At the time the ball was pushed forward to start the backswing, there is increased activity in the bilateral sacrospinalis and slightly in the external oblique muscles indicating that they may have acted to support the rib cage.

Because four steps (right, left, right, left) were involved in the bowling approach, while only a weight transference back to the right foot and then a step forward onto the left was used in the throw, it was obvious that there would be a difference in the activity of the leg muscles. However, when the records were compared, the muscular activity for the throw is seen to be very similar to that of the last two steps of the bowling approach. The difference lies in the fact that the potentials indicating the right step (during the backswing) of the throw last longer than those indicating the right step (third step) of the bowling approach.

The abdominal muscles acted very similarly in the two activities. The only difference that is apparent is in the left external oblique muscle which was more active at the beginning of the forward swing in bowling and nearer release in the throw. A similarity is also apparent in the records of the sacrospinalis. The one real difference is the greater activity seen in the left sacrospinalis during the bowling backswing, indicating the involvement of this muscle in the stabilization of the trunk against the pull of the heavy ball on the right side of the body.

Chapter V

Overhand Pattern

ELECTROMYOGRAMS during the performance of the overhand throw, badminton clear, and tennis serve appeared to substantiate the similarity of movement patterns. Therefore, the overhand throw is analyzed in considerable detail and similarities and differences of the badminton clear and tennis serve are discussed.

OVERHAND THROW

Shoulder Girdle and Upper Extremity Muscles

Preparatory Stance

Prior to the act of throwing overhand, the subject stood with her trunk very slightly flexed and head erect. Her upper arms were held in slight forward flexion with flexed forearms and both hands supported the ball (Fig. 14).

The muscles showing increased electrical activity to maintain this position of the upper extremity are the bilateral anterior deltoid, left serratus anterior, clavicular portion of the left pectoralis, bilateral biceps and brachioradialis, wrist and finger extensors and left flexors (Fig. 15, p. 37). Action in the right and left middle and lower trapezius is also seen. These muscles probably were contributing to stabilization of the shoulder girdle. The upper trapezius was slightly active in maintaining the head in an erect position.

The Throw

Initiation of the throw is evidenced by small bursts of electrical activity in the right serratus anterior, brachioradialis, and wrist and finger flexors, and the beginning of a crescendo in action potentials of the anterior deltoid which are concurrent with cessation of electrical activity in the clavicular portion of the left pectoralis muscle and increased activity in the left middle and lower trapezius. Changes in action potentials of the left extremity were apparently concerned with retracting the hand from holding the ball. During the backswing, the right extremity was abducted and externally rotated with the elbow flexed and wrist extended, while the left shoulder girdle was stabilized and the left extremity was abducted with the elbow bent. Since the trunk was rotated to the right, this put the left arm in a position somewhat below shoulder height and pointing in the general direction of the target. Activity is seen in the left posterior and middle deltoid, triceps, sternocleidomastoid, and upper, middle, and lower trapezius. A comparison of the muscle patterns of the right and left sides demonstrates the reciprocal action of the upper extremities during the backswing.

The right anterior and middle deltoid were involved in abducting the arm, and the brachioradialis and biceps in flexing the elbow. As the body rotated right, the left extremity did not follow but was held back in an abducted position. Activity is seen in the records of the left posterior deltoid and triceps. Right wrist and finger flexors and extensors were undoubtedly responsible for the grip of the ball. Also the electrical activity seen in the right and left middle trapezius was probably effective in re-

FIGURE 14. OVERHAND THROW—Frames from motion pictures of subject's performance.

OVERHAND THROW

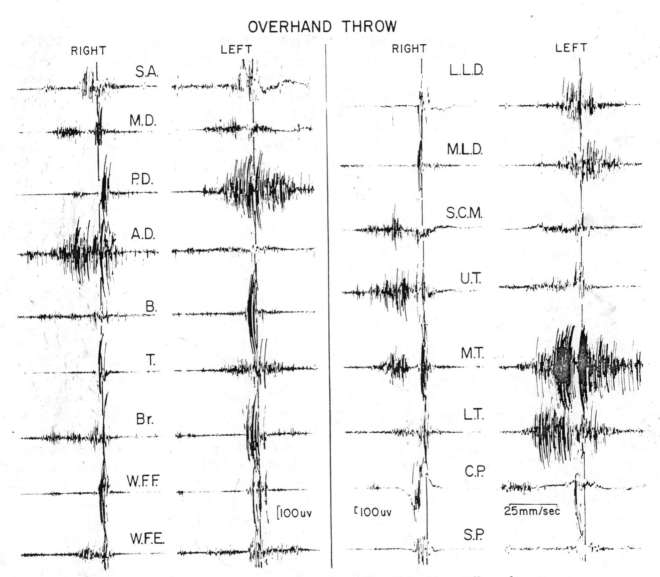

FIGURE 15. OVERHAND THROW—Activity in muscles of shoulder girdle and upper extremity. See Figure 3 for muscle symbols.

tracting and stabilizing the shoulder girdle. Bilateral action of the upper trapezius and sternocleidomastoid extended the neck and elevated the shoulder girdle and maintained the head position facing the general direction of the target. The serratus anterior was active in fixing the vertebral border of the scapula for the action of the above muscles.

During the backswing, the body was rotated to the right as the trunk extended. The action in the middle, lower, and upper trapezius muscles and the left latissimus dorsi may have contributed to these movements. The activity in the left latissimus dorsi during the backswing may indicate that the subject bent her trunk slightly to the right at the top of the backswing. (See also back, abdominal, and leg action.)

Bursts of activity in the right posterior deltoid, lower trapezius and wrist extensors seem to indicate the approach to the top of the backswing. The lower trapezius contributed to final shoulder retraction, the posterior deltoid to extension of the upper arm, and the wrist and finger extensors to full extension of the wrist. Activity in the middle deltoid, upper and middle trapezius, and brachioradialis diminishes at this time.

An instantaneous pause in the activity of the left middle trapezius and a burst in the clavicular portion of the pectorals mark the top of the backswing and reversal of movement. Increased activity in the left latissimus dorsi occurs at the beginning of the trunk rotation toward the left, and thus the initiation of the forward movement of the throw. (This activity is concurrent with increased activity in the left sacrospinalis, right and left external obliques, and slightly ahead of the left rectus abdominis.) Increased activity in the right serratus anterior and pectoralis major muscles follows immediately and probably contributed to the movement of the shoulder girdle forward in the direction of the target. Immediately thereafter, during the time that the flexed arm was moved forward, renewed action is seen in the right anterior deltoid, biceps, and brachioradialis. Immediately before release, strong contractions are seen

in the right medial portion of the latissimus dorsi, the right triceps, and the wrist and finger flexors, followed immediately by the extensor muscles.

It is interesting to note that during the forward swing and release, there is considerably greater activity in the left biceps and brachioradialis than in the left triceps, while the comparative magnitudes are reversed in the right (throwing) extremity. This would be anticipated since the left elbow was flexing and the right was extending. The activity seen in the left serratus anterior during the forward swing of the throwing arm undoubtedly was involved in fixing the left scapula for adduction action of the left arm. At the start of the forward swing of the right extremity, a burst of activity in the left brachioradialis, followed by the same in the biceps, is seen indicating the bending of the left elbow as the arm was adducted. The action seen in the left wrist and finger flexors and extensors may have set this wrist, and thus reflexly facilitated contraction of the right. A decrease in activity of the left lower trapezius occurs during the forward movement of the right arm. At release, left triceps activity acts in braking the flexing motion of that arm and activity in the middle and lower trapezius and latissimus dorsi muscles indicates their contribution to the resistance of forces tending to flex the trunk.

Immediately before the point of release there is a decrease in activity in the right serratus anterior and the clavicular portion of the right and left pectoralis and at the same time bursts of action potentials occur in the right middle and lower trapezius which probably contributed to checking sharply the forward movement of the throwing arm. The timing of the sharp bursts in the right latissimus dorsi suggests that this muscle may also act to check the forward movement of the arm.

Activity in the three portions of the right deltoid show a distinct pattern throughout the throw. The anterior and middle portions are active during the backswing with the posterior coming in somewhat toward the last part. The anterior portion is very active during the forward movement of the arm and the posterior contracts during the follow-through, undoubtedly to check the movement. Also, the burst of activity in the right triceps before and during release is immediately followed by a short but very strong burst of activity in the brachioradialis, indicating a braking action to protect the elbow joint. Still pictures taken in the laboratory show that the elbow was at an angle of approximately 105 degrees at the moment of release (Fig. 16).

After release of the ball, as gravity and momentum carried the arm downward, a diminution of electrical activity occurs in the right shoulder girdle and upper extremity muscles. Activity in the left shoulder girdle and upper extremity diminishes as the subject recovered from the follow-through and returned to the erect position.

Back, Abdominal, and Lower Extremity Muscles

Preparatory Stance and Backward Weight Transference

At the beginning of the record, evidence of the subject's shifting added weight to her left foot before she shifted it all to the right foot is seen in the muscle action evoked in the legs (Fig. 17, p. 41). Activity is seen in the right soleus, gastrocnemius, peroneus longus, tensor fasciae latae, and hamstrings. There is also slight activity in the left hamstrings. This minimal amount of electrical activity of the hamstrings in the preparatory position probably is attributable to stabilization at the hip since the subject started the backswing from a very slightly forward-flexed position. This is followed by considerable activity in the left soleus, peroneus longus, toe extensors, sartorius, rectus femoris and slight activity in the left external hamstrings. This apparently indicates the taking of the weight onto the left foot and the beginning of the push which then transferred it to the right foot. At this time there is an increase in the activity of the left external hamstrings and a cessation of activity in the right hamstrings, but considerable activity in the

right tibialis anterior and some in the toe extensors.

Simultaneously, there is increased activity in the right sacrospinalis which suggests that this muscle was involved in rotating the trunk and in stabilizing the pelvis for the taking of weight on the right foot. The right hamstrings then become active again, probably to flex the knee while the continued activity of the tibialis anterior and toe extensors undoubtedly dorsiflexed the foot. This is followed by a second burst in the left soleus, peroneus longus, and toe extensors concurrent with increased activity in the right and left gracilis, right toe extensors, bursts of activity in the right soleus, gastrocnemius, and a slight increase in activity of the peroneus longus, tensor fasciae latae, sartorius, rectus femoris, and vastus lateralis. This is immediately followed by increased activity in the left sartorius and then the rectus femoris. This seems to indicate the final transference of weight to the right foot.

The Throw

As noted above, immediately prior to the backward movement of the right upper extremity, the weight was shifted to the right foot and, as the body rotated to the right, the weight was transferred completely onto it. The bilateral action of the sacrospinalis and the activity of the left external oblique suggests that these muscles were involved in the rotation of the trunk to the right and in supporting the trunk in a partially flexed position. Activity in these muscles is seen throughout the back and forward swing of the right arm. However, during the rotation of the trunk to the left in the forward swing, considerable activity in the left rectus abdominis and right external oblique, and slight activity in the right rectus abdominis also is seen. In addition to their contribution to trunk rotation, these muscles probably were acting to stabilize the trunk, rib cage, and pelvis for action of the extremities. The sacrospinalis muscles are extremely active during follow-through as they apparently were involved in resisting forces (momentum and grav-

FIGURE 16. OVERHAND THROW—Point of release. Note angle of elbow. (Still picture taken during recording of lower extremity muscle activity.)

OVERHAND THROW

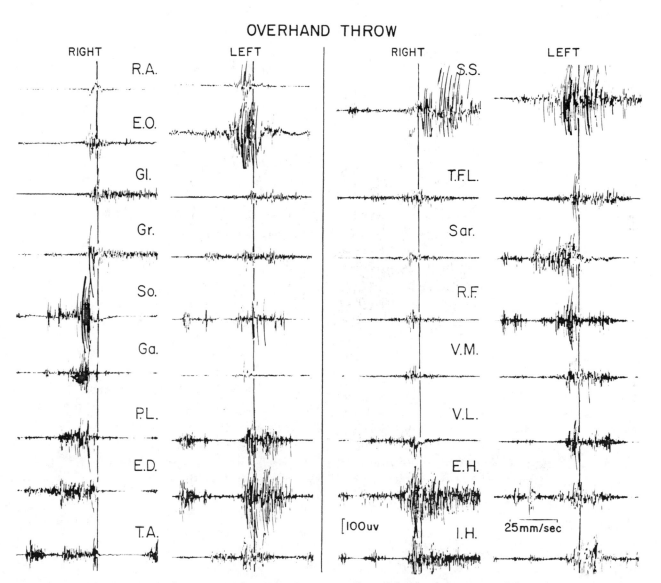

FIGURE 17. OVERHAND THROW—Activity in muscles of back, abdomen, and lower extremity. See Figure 4 for muscle symbols.

ity) which tended to cause further trunk flexion. On follow-through, this subject supported herself on her left extremity with the right extended off the floor and the trunk flexed forward.

The greatest magnitude of electrical activity in the right thigh and leg muscles occurs at the top of the backswing, apparently as they pushed the body weight forward onto the left extremity. The sharp drop in magnitude of electrical activity in the right soleus, gastrocnemius, and peroneus longus coincides with the beginning of the forward swing of the right arm.

The complete transfer of body weight as the ball was released is evidenced by the cessation of electrical activity in the muscles of the right lower leg and by the increased activity in the muscles of the left lower extremity as they acted to maintain balance of the body weight.

During the follow-through, activity is evident in all muscles of the left extremity (gastrocnemius very slight*), but in the right leg only the hamstrings, gluteus maximus, gracilis, and tensor fasciae latae show more than very slight activity. These were involved in holding the extremity off the floor in an extended position. This was the situation until the subject resumed the normal standing position.

---

*Left gastrocnemius electrodes apparently had been loosened (see explanation, p. 7).

BADMINTON CLEAR

Because the ceiling in the laboratory was too low for a high-arched "set-up" of the shuttlecock, a bent pin on the end of a piece of string was inserted through the feathers and the shuttle was suspended from the ceiling at the height that permitted the subject to reach it with the center of her racket when she extended fully (Fig. 18, p. 43). When struck, the shuttle flew off readily. Photographs of the subject hitting a moving shuttle and the suspended one were comparable (Fig. 19).

When electromyograms of the badminton clear are compared to those of the overhand throw, a great deal of similarity in the general pattern of muscle function, both timing and magnitude, is apparent.

Shoulder Girdle and Upper Extremity Muscles

Preparatory Stance

As the subject prepared to hit the suspended shuttle, she held her racket in the right hand with its head resting in her left hand. Her general body position was very similar to that assumed preceding the overhand throw. The muscular activity recorded at the extreme left edge of each record reflects this similarity (Fig. 20, p. 46). There may have been slightly more activity in the right serratus anterior, right wrist and finger flexors, and left lower trapezius, and less in the right biceps and left wrist and finger flexors and right extensors before she started the clear than before the throw. Again, as in the badminton serve, slightly more activity in the right wrist and finger flexors was required to grasp the racket than to hold the ball. However, the left hand was more active in helping support the ball than the racket.

The Stroke

As in the throw, the initiation of the stroke is apparent in the increased potentials in the right serratus anterior and wrist and finger flexors. The same cessation of activity in the clavicular portion of the left pectoralis muscle and increase in the left middle and lower trapezius is seen in the records of both the clear and the overhand throw, indicating the retraction of the left extremity from the racket in the clear, and the ball in the throw. However, unlike the throw, the right brachioradialis diminishes at this time while the right triceps and posterior deltoid burst briefly to extend the elbow and initiate retraction of the right arm. The racket was dropped down and back for the clear, but the arm was flexed as it was drawn backward for the throw and thus more constant activity is seen in the biceps and brachioradialis during the backswing of the throw. The flexion of the right arm to drop the racket behind the body for the clear is seen in the later bursts of activ-

FIGURE 18. Subject measuring the height of the suspended shuttle.

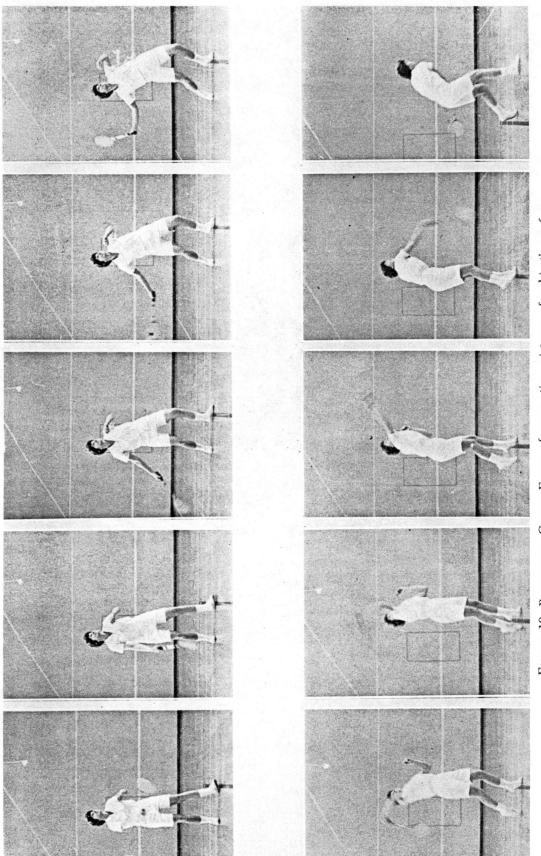

FIGURE 19. BADMINTON CLEAR—Frames from motion pictures of subject's performance. Subject was instructed by cameraman to begin her stroke as she was measuring the height of the shuttle. Therefore the preparatory position taken in the laboratory before the stroke when the electromyograms were recorded is not shown in the picture sequence.

ity in the right brachioradialis and biceps on the badminton record. Maximum extension of the right wrist during the badminton backswing is obvious in the larger potentials of the wrist and finger extensors.

Forceful extension of the right arm to swing the racket up to contact the shuttle is evidenced by the burst in the right triceps which appears to begin slightly earlier than the burst of activity in this muscle to extend the arm for the overhand throw. This would be anticipated because the arm extension starts sooner in the former skill since in the throw the arm is not extended until after the shoulders have been rotated to face the direction of the throw. In fact, the arm is not fully extended until after the ball has been released. As indicated earlier, this subject's elbow was at approximately a 105-degree angle at release. In both skills there is a burst of activity in the brachioradialis at the moment of release (impact), but the burst of activity in the right wrist and finger flexors is slightly earlier and lasts longer in the badminton clear.

It is interesting to note that the overhand throw required more activity in the right anterior deltoid while the left is more active during the badminton clear. The right anterior deltoid is more active during the backswing of the throw because the arm was abducted and outwardly rotated while in the badminton clear the racket dropped down and backward before being lifted behind the body. It is more active during the forward swing of the throw because the arm was maintained in the abducted and rotated position (elbow shoulder height) as the elbow was brought forward, while in the clear the arm was extended upward. To balance the activity in the right arm, the left was abducted (deltoids) and somewhat retracted (triceps) for both skills. However, the activity in these muscles is greater for the clear. The left posterior deltoid is more active during the follow-through of the throw. The left sternocleidomastoid is considerably more active in the badminton clear than the throw. This is undoubtedly because the subject was required to look more

directly upward in order to see the shuttle at a time when the body was rotated to the right.

Electromyograms of the serratus anterior, right middle deltoid, right posterior deltoid, left biceps, right latissimus dorsi, right upper, middle and lower trapezius, and left pectoral muscles show almost identical timing and magnitude for the two skills. While the activity of the right pectoralis muscles is very similar, they begin to burst slightly earlier in the badminton clear.

Back, Abdominal, and Lower Extremity Muscles

Preparatory Stance

Apparently slightly more weight was on the right foot as the subject prepared to hit the shuttle than when she was preparing to throw overhand. Slightly more activity is seen in the right peroneus longus, toe extensors, tensor fasciae latae, and hamstring muscles (Fig. 21, p. 47). Other than this, the action potentials appear to be the same for the two skills.

The Stroke

The same general pattern of weight transference, back to the right foot and then forward to the left, is again seen. However, there are two major differences between the action for the clear and the throw. In the badminton clear, the subject more actively pushed her weight onto the left foot and as the left foot took the weight, she pushed up onto her toes, thus reducing to a minimum the amount of weight still supported by the right foot before impact. The greater magnitude of potentials for the right soleus, gastrocnemius, peroneus longus, and toe extensors during the badminton clear; the sudden decrease in activity of the latter two considerably before impact (not seen in the throw); and the simultaneous burst of activity in the left soleus, peroneus longus, and toe extensors (much more active than in the throw) indicate the pushing of the weight up onto the left toes for the contact with the shuttle at full extension. In general, the right quadriceps, tensor fasciae latae, sartorius, and gracilis are more active (to extend the knee)

BADMINTON CLEAR

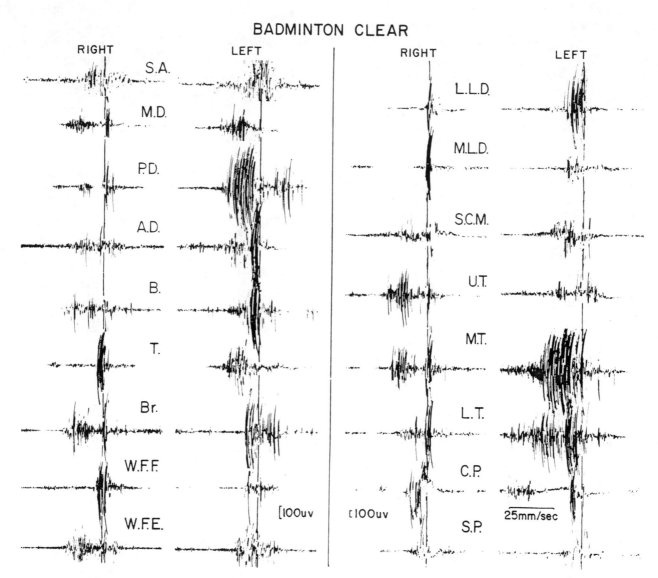

FIGURE 20. BADMINTON CLEAR—Activity in muscles of shoulder girdle and upper extremity. See Figure 3 for muscle symbols. Note the similarity of pattern for both extremities between this activity and the overhand throw (Fig. 15).

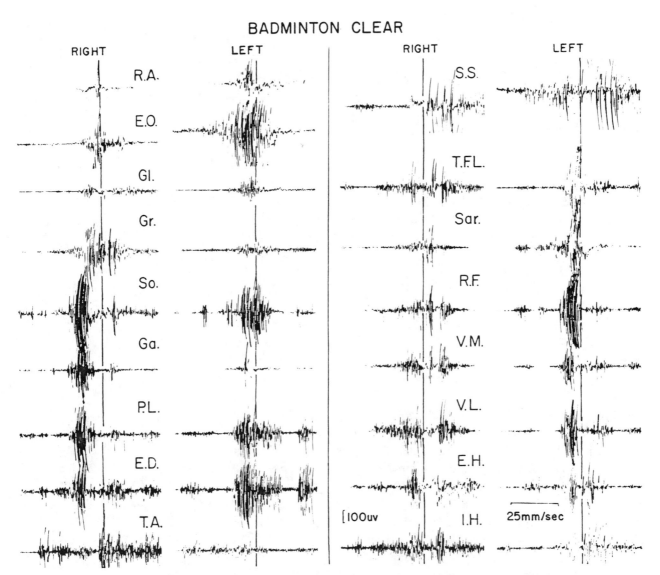

FIGURE 21. BADMINTON CLEAR—Activity in muscles of back, abdomen, and lower extremity. See Figure 4 for muscle symbols. Greater extensor activity of the lower extremity is noted in this electromyogram than in the records for the overhand throw (Fig. 17).

before contact with the shuttle than release of the ball. Also, there is greater extensor activity of the thigh muscles on the left although the patterns are quite similar.

The other real difference lies in the fact that the subject stepped through with the right foot on follow-through in the clear, but extended her right hip and held the right extremity backward off the floor in the throw. Therefore, during early follow-through, action potentials which are not obvious on the throw record are seen on the badminton record in the right soleus, peroneus longus, toe extensors, and tibialis anterior. The activity of the right hamstrings, important in supporting the lifted leg in the throw, is less in the clear, as these muscles acted with other muscles of the thigh and leg to catch the body weight as the extremity swung through.

Patterns of electrical activity in the abdominal muscles during the performance of the two skills are similar although greater magnitudes are evident in the records of the clear. Hyperextension of the trunk at the top of the backswing of the badminton clear is indicated by stronger activity in the external oblique muscles as they were involved in supporting the trunk against the pull of gravity. This is more obvious in the left muscle than the right since the body was rotated toward the right. The break in action of the left sacrospinalis at the beginning of the forward movement simultaneous with increased activity of the left rectus abdominis, right external obliques, and continued activity of the left external obliques suggests the forward flexion and upward stretch during the forward swing of the badminton clear as contrasted with the more rotary movement of the throw. In both skills the left abdominals are more active than the right, probably because of the need for stabilization. Action of the right extremity muscles during the forward swing is reflected in the pattern of activity in the right and left sacrospinalis. In both activities the sacrospinalis muscles were important in supporting the trunk against gravity's pull during follow-through, but in addition the throw required greater stabilization of the pelvis as the right leg was held extended off the ground.

TENNIS SERVE

The relatively low ceiling of the laboratory made the toss for the tennis service difficult. The ball had to be tossed to the exact height of the hit. If tossed higher, it rebounded from the ceiling, making contact impossible. Therefore, the subject may not have extended to her fullest reach in performing the service. Since the muscular activity during the serve is so similar to that during the badminton clear, the following discussion is concerned mainly with the differences between the records of the two activities.

Shoulder Girdle and Upper Extremity Muscles

Preparatory Stance

In general, the muscular activity as the subject prepared for the service was very similar to that seen before she executed the badminton clear (Fig. 23, p. 50). This would be anticipated since she held a racket in front of her body.

Although she rested the head of the racket in her left hand for the clear, she held the balls in her left hand against the racket for the serve. Obvious differences in the electromyograms during the preparation for the two activities are seen in the greater potentials of the right pectoralis major and the left anterior deltoid, and slightly greater activity in the middle and lower left trapezius as she was anticipating the tennis toss.

The Serve

During the execution of the tennis serve, the muscular activity in the right arm and shoulder girdle is almost identical to that during the badminton clear. Very few real differences are apparent in the electromyogram. The early burst of the serratus anterior is more apparent in the serve record than in the records for either the clear or the overhand throw. The greater mag-

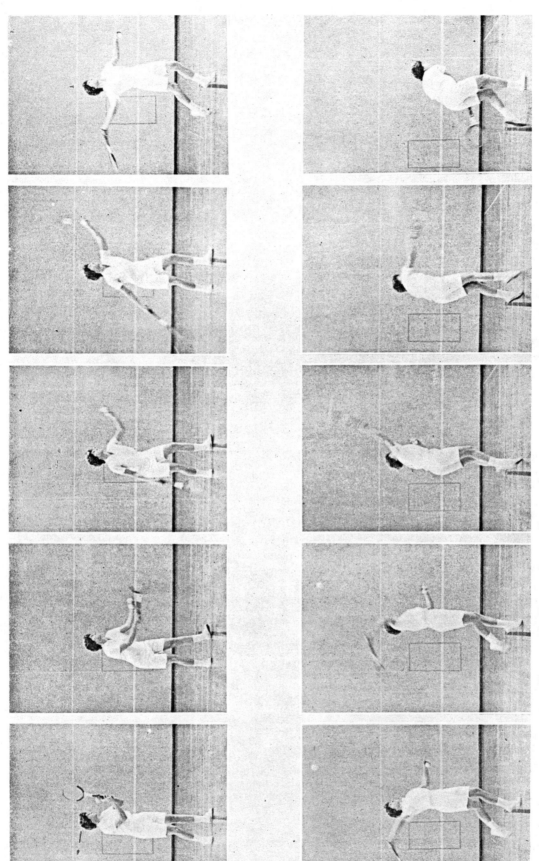

FIGURE 22. TENNIS SERVE—Frames from motion pictures of the subject's performance.

TENNIS SERVE

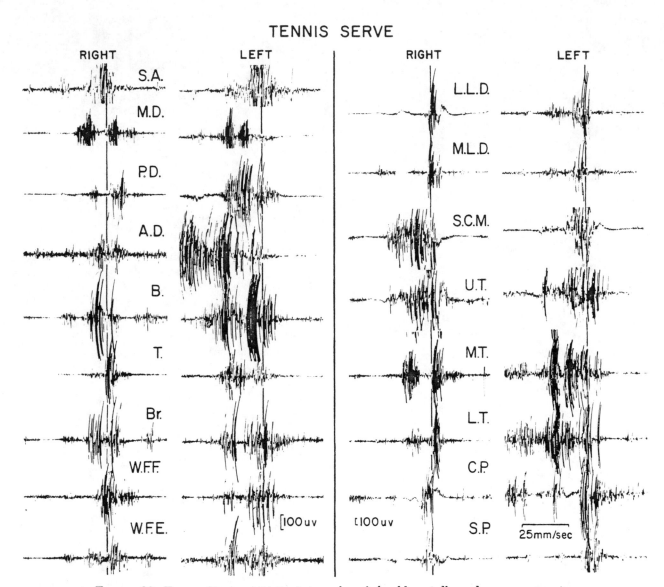

FIGURE 23. TENNIS SERVE—Activity in muscles of shoulder girdle and upper extremity. See Figure 3 for muscle symbols. The toss of the ball is evident in increased activity of the left arm and forearm muscles. The right muscle pattern is very similar to the badminton clear (Fig. 20).

nitude of the second burst of the biceps may be caused by the greater weight of the tennis racket. The activity in the wrist and finger flexors may have begun a bit earlier in the serve while that in the extensors is considerably less during the backswing. The timing indicates that the extensor muscles acted concurrently with the biceps and brachioradialis during the serve.

At the time of the toss of the ball with the left hand, there is a burst of activity in the right sternocleidomastoid muscle. This activity is considerably less in the records of the badminton clear and the overhand throw (Figs. 15 & 20). Both the right and left sternocleidomastoid muscles show more activity during the forward swing of the tennis racket than during the throw or clear. The greater activity in the right sternocleidomastoid muscle during the backswing for the tennis serve may have been required to stabilize the shoulder against the momentum of the backward drop of the heavier racket. It is interesting to note that, while less activity is seen in the right upper trapezius during the backswing of the serve than of the other two activities, there is greater activity in this muscle and the sternocleidomastoid during the forward swing. It is possible that the drop of the heavier racket caused greater momentum, which relieved the upper trapezius to some extent in lifting the racket on backswing, but the heavy racket required greater effort for the forward swing.

The lesser activity in the sternocleidomastoid during the throw than either the serve or clear is undoubtedly due to the fact that the head was maintained in a level position rather than being tilted backward as in both the clear and the serve.

The ball toss is clearly apparent in the records of the muscles of the left arm and shoulder. The anterior deltoid, biceps, brachioradialis, wrist and finger flexors and extensors, trapezius, and pectorals all burst simultaneously. Also,

there is greater activity in the serratus anterior and latissimus dorsi muscles at this time. The left anterior deltoid records show much less activity during forward swing of the tennis racket than of the badminton racket, particularly around contact. Following the toss, the left arm was dropping from the position of following the ball upward while it was held in abduction during the clear.

Back, Abdominal, and Lower Extremity Muscles
Preparatory Stance

Less muscular activity in the lower extremity muscles is evident as the subject prepared to serve the tennis ball than is seen on the records of either the clear or the overhand throw (Fig. 24, p. 52). The left soleus, peroneus longus, tibialis anterior, and internal hamstrings show some activity as do the right hamstrings and the bilateral sacrospinalis muscles, the latter required by the slightly forward-flexed position of the trunk.

The Serve

The pattern of muscular activity in the lower extremities during the serve is very similar to that of the clear. Again the subject's high reach and step through with the right foot following contact is obvious. The fact that she did not lean backward with arched back and flexed hips and knees to the same degree on the backswing for the serve as for the clear is evident in the lesser magnitude of potentials for the thigh muscles during the backswing of the serve. However, the momentum of the heavier racket must have been effective in bringing the body weight through with greater force since the potentials for the muscles in the right leg are greater as the right foot took the weight following contact with the tennis ball than the badminton shuttle.

Greater activity of the abdominal muscles was required by the heavier implement. This is apparent in the rectus abdominis muscles, particularly the right.

TENNIS SERVE

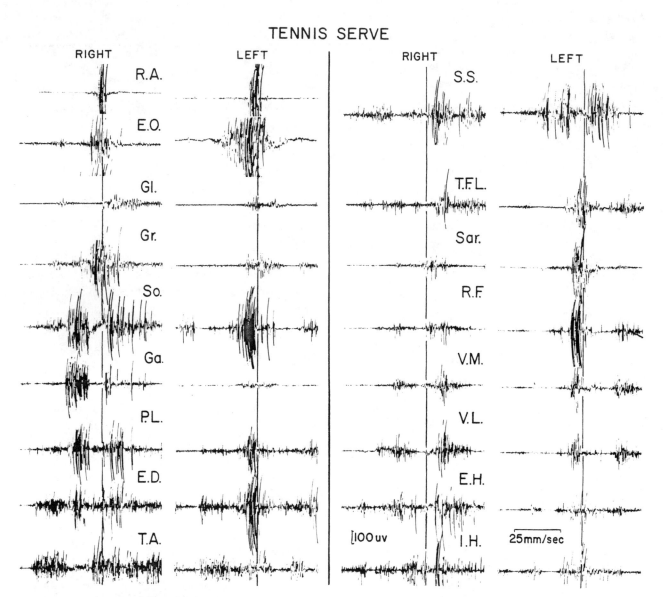

FIGURE 24. TENNIS SERVE—Activity in muscles of back, abdomen, and lower extremity. See Figure 4 for muscle symbols. The patterns of muscular activity are similar to those of the badminton clear (Fig. 21) and not unlike those for the overhand throw (Fig. 17).

Chapter VI

Sidearm Pattern

THE records of muscular activity during the performance of the basketball throw, tennis drive, and batting appear to substantiate the similarity of movement patterns noted by Broer. Therefore, the basketball throw is analyzed in considerable detail and the similarities and differences between this throw and the tennis drive and batting are discussed.

Because of the essentially vertical swing, golf has been considered by some people to be an adaptation of the underhand pattern. The results of this study indicate that the patterns of electrical activity during the golf swing are more like those found for batting than for any of the underhand activities studied. For this reason, the golf analysis is included in this section. The similarity in body positions at various points in the golf and batting movements, particularly in the positions at the end of the follow-through, is interesting (Figs. 31, 34). However, the patterns of muscular activity were found to be sufficiently different to warrant a more detailed analysis.

BASKETBALL THROW

Shoulder Girdle and Upper Extremity Muscles

Preparatory Stance

Muscles acting to maintain the position prior to the basketball throw are seen to the extreme left of the electromyograms (Fig. 26, pg. 55). The ball was held in front and to the right of the body, with the left shoulder somewhat forward of the right. The elbows were flexed (Fig. 25). As would be anticipated, the bilateral forward flexors of the shoulder (pectoralis major) and of the arm (anterior deltoid and biceps) were active. The biceps, with the brachioradialis muscles, maintained the flexed position of the elbows as the wrist and finger extensors, with the left wrist and finger flexors, supported the ball. Although the activity appears greater in the left muscle group, the calibration of the two extremities is different. (Note "uv," Fig. 26). Activity in the shoulder girdle muscles occurred for stabilization and these muscles with the external obliques and sacrospinalis (p. 57) also functioned to support the very slightly flexed trunk. Bilateral upper trapezius action was involved in maintaining the head in a position facing the target.

The Throw

Initiation of the backward swing and trunk rotation to the right is evidenced by bursts of activity in the left serratus anterior and pectoralis major with gradual increased activity in the right middle trapezius (see also right sacrospinalis, Fig. 27, p. 57). Bilateral action in the upper trapezius supported the shoulder girdle and maintained the head facing the target as the trunk rotated.

During the backswing, the left hand was removed from supporting the ball and the right extremity assumed complete control. Action potentials in the right anterior deltoid, biceps, brachioradialis, and wrist and finger flexors and

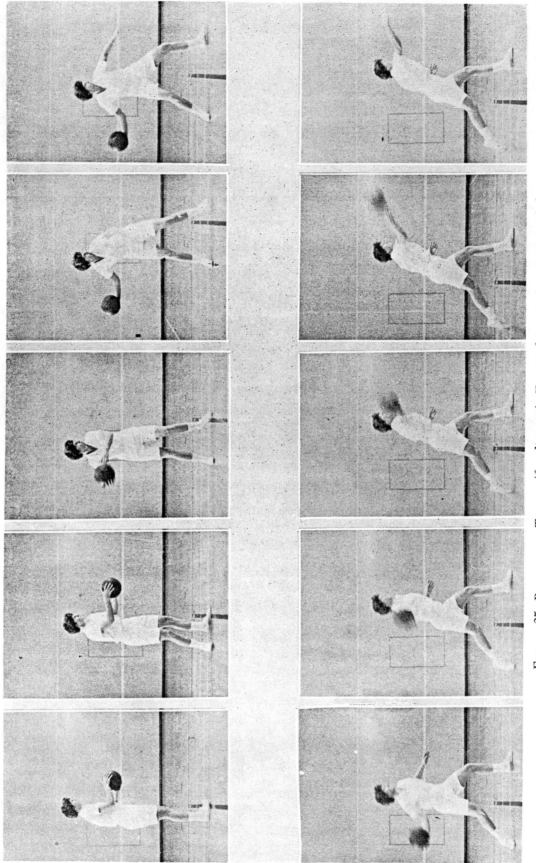

FIGURE 25. BASKETBALL THROW (for distance)—Frames from motion pictures of the subject's performance. (Sidearm throw.)

BASKETBALL THROW

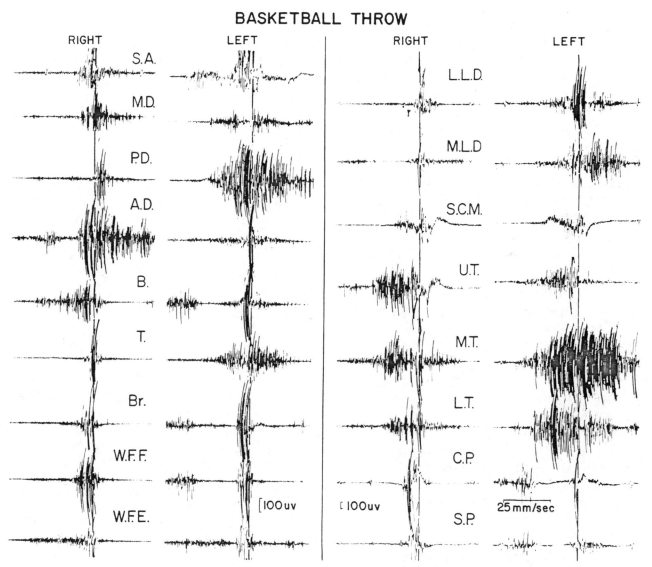

FIGURE 26. BASKETBALL THROW (for distance)—Activity in muscles of shoulder girdle and upper extremity. See Figure 3 for muscle symbols.

extensors increase instantaneously before electrical activity in the left biceps, brachioradialis, and wrist and finger flexors gradually diminishes. After the right extremity attained complete control of the ball, there is a slight diminution in the right anterior deltoid. At this time, increased activity occurs in the middle and lower trapezius to move the shoulder girdle posteriorly and thereby extend the arm to a maximum position before the forward swing of the throw. Electrical activity in the left serratus anterior and pectoralis major continues momentarily and then the former decreases, probably to act as a stabilizer, and the latter ceases as the middle and lower trapezius retracted the shoulder girdle. The left middle and posterior deltoid, latissimus dorsi, and triceps gradually retracted that arm and extended the elbow. The latissimus dorsi may also have been contributing to rotation of the trunk to the left.

The beginning of the forward swing is characterized by rotation of the trunk toward the left. The extremity carrying the ball was held with the arm away from the body and in slight forward flexion primarily by action of the long head of the biceps. The arm did not start its forward movement until after the left rotation of the trunk was well underway. Increased activity in the right and left serratus anterior, right pectoralis major, anterior deltoid, and wrist and finger flexors immediately follows bursts in the trunk muscles. Prior to this time, there is a slight diminution in the magnitude of the electrical activity in the right anterior and middle deltoid and middle and lower trapezius, which later burst again. This action of these muscles may have assisted in guiding the arm and stabilizing the shoulder girdle. Activity in the right biceps gradually builds up through the backswing to maintain the supinated, slightly-flexed forearm with a maximum crescendo as the upper extremity was starting the forward movement. Bilateral activity in the upper trapezius during rotation of the body to the left contributed to maintaining a level position of the shoulder girdle. Maximum action of the triceps

occurs immediately before release as the arm was extended flinging the basketball into the air. The wrist and finger flexors are very active during the forward swing and release. The activity of the right latissimus dorsi probably was concerned with internal rotation of the arm at release and possibly a braking action on the arm.

Muscles of the left shoulder girdle were probably active to stabilize the shoulder girdle and rib cage and to maintain the erect trunk during the forward movement of the arm into the follow-through. As the trunk rotated, the upper trapezius and sternocleidomastoid muscles were active in maintaining the position of the head toward the direction of the target. At release, the pattern of muscle activity suggests that both shoulder girdles were strongly drawn into forward flexion; the left possibly to reinforce the right. Reinforcement from the contralateral side is also evident in the strong activity of the left wrist and finger flexors and extensors as they contracted with the right. The flexing of the left arm during the forward swing of the right arm is obvious in the bursts of activity in the left brachioradialis and biceps.

After release, activity in the muscles of the throwing forearm diminishes rapidly. The deltoids, serratus anterior, and trapezius muscles continued to hold the arm in abduction and to move it in the direction of the throw. The left latissimus dorsi continued to be active in the follow-through phase to assist in trunk rotation. Activity in the left shoulder girdle occurred to further retract that shoulder as the right one was projected. Diminution of activity in all muscles occurs after the follow-through phase.

Back, Abdominal, and Lower Extremity Muscles
Preparatory Stance

Electrical activity in the leg muscles was seemingly minimal as the subject prepared for this throw (Fig. 27, p. 57). Some activity in the hamstrings, bilaterally, suggests these muscles maintained a slight degree of knee and hip flexion. The external oblique and sacrospinalis demonstrated minor activity, probably to sta-

BASKETBALL THROW

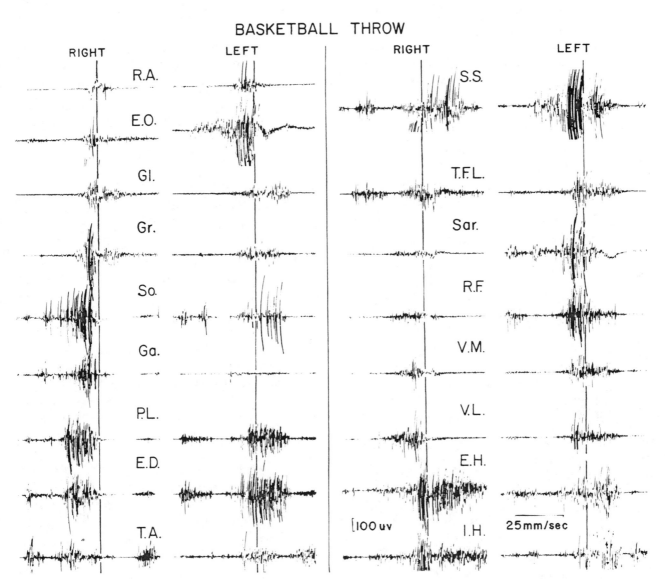

FIGURE 27. BASKETBALL THROW (for distance) —Activity in muscles of back, abdomen, and lower extremity. See Figure 4 for muscle symbols.

bilize the rib cage and trunk in a very slightly flexed position.

The Throw

Transfer of weight to the right foot is evidenced by bursts of activity in the leg muscles, mainly the right tibialis anterior and bilateral soleus, peroneus longus, and toe extensors. Bursts of activity also occur simultaneously in the right tensor fasciae latae and left sartorius, rectus femoris, and hamstrings.

A second burst of activity, noticed primarily in the left and right soleus and the right gastrocnemius,* preoneus longus, toe extensors, and left sartorius occurs at the time the left hand released the basketball. Bursts in the right extremity may have occurred to stabilize this extremity. Activity in the left may have been associated with the subject's effort to keep this foot so that the toe was pointed more or less toward the target.

As the weight was transferred onto the right foot, increased activity of the left external oblique and the right sacrospinalis muscles occurs. This suggests the initiation of trunk rotation and lateral flexion to the right. As the left hand was released from the ball, electrical activity diminshes in the right and begins to increase in the left sacrospinalis, probably to support the laterally flexed trunk.

At the top of the backswing, the left extremity was extended at the knee and hip and externally rotated, probably by action of the left sartorius and external hamstrings. The right extremity was flexed at the hip and knee and internally rotated, probably by action of the tensor fasciae latae and internal hamstrings.

The beginning of rotation of the body to the left, indicating the beginning of the forward throw, probably occurred at the time of the

---

*Left gastrocnemius electrodes apparently had been loosened (see explanation, p. 7).

marked increase of activity in the left external oblique and sacrospinalis. The former muscle probably acted to raise the trunk to an erect position as the latter muscle, with the right external oblique and left rectus abdominis, contributed to the rotary movement. The weight was transferred from the right to the left extremity by gradually increased action in all right lower extremity muscles. Immediately before transfer the left extremity was lifted from the floor and, with the exception of the sartorius which was probably involved in maintaining the leg position (hip flexion and lateral rotation), there is a period of relative quiescence in the left extremity. This is followed immediately by an increase of activity in all muscles as the weight was transferred.

By the time the ball was released, there is relatively little activity in the right leg muscles, while the left lower extremity muscles are active in supporting the body weight. As the ball was released, the right leg was extended at the hip, slightly flexed at the knee, and plantar flexed at the foot. The position of the hip and knee may be attributed to the gluteus maximus and hamstring action. The left external oblique and sacrospinalis show tremendous bursts of activity during the forward throw, a pause at release, and lesser activity in the follow-through. The right external oblique and the left rectus abdominis are active during the throw and diminish at the release. The right sacrospinalis is active to a lesser degree during the throw, but more active after release, as is the right rectus abdominis, although the activity in the latter is slight. These two muscles probably acted to check the body momentum. Action of the abdominals may have contributed also to stabilization of the rib cage and pelvis during upper and lower extremity movements. The sacrospinalis muscles may have been effective also in stabilizing the pelvis.

TENNIS DRIVE

For the tennis drive the subject tossed the ball and allowed it to bounce before striking it (Fig. 28).

Shoulder Girdle and Upper Extremity Muscles
Preparatory Stance

As the subject stood before tossing the ball,

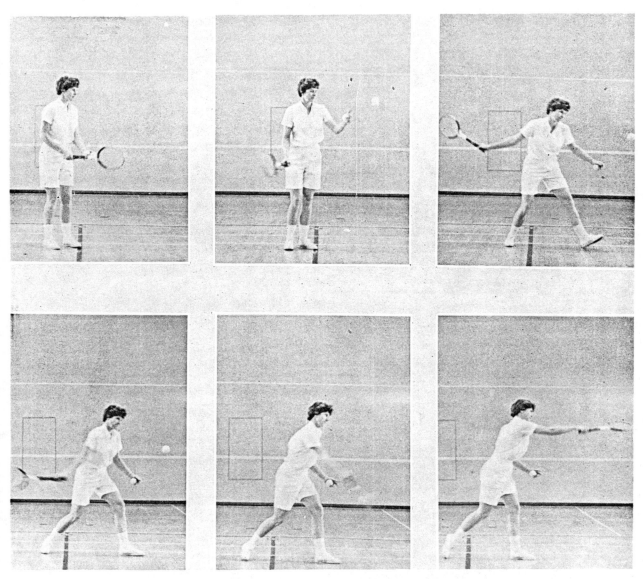

FIGURE 28. TENNIS DRIVE—Frames from motion pictures of subject's performance. During recording of the electromyograms the subject lifted the right toes off the floor briefly during follow-through.

there was some activity in the bilateral serratus anterior, biceps, left triceps, right brachioradialis, bilateral latissimus dorsi (medial portion), left trapezius, and very slight activity in the middle and lower portions of the right trapezius muscles (Fig. 29, p. 61). The grip of the racket is evident in the records of the right wrist and finger flexors and extensors. It is interesting to note that the extensors of the wrist and fingers on the left show activity, but that of the flexors is negligible. Apparently the subject held the ball on her hand before the toss rather than gripping it with the fingers.

The Drive

The toss of the ball preceded the backswing of the drive and thus bursts of activity are seen in the left anterior deltoid, biceps, brachioradialis, wrist and finger flexor and extensor, and trapezius muscles. These bursts are followed immediately by action in the left middle deltoid, triceps, lateral portion of the latissimus dorsi and continued extensive action of the lower portion of the trapezius as the left arm was retracted after the toss of the ball.

This activity is followed by increased potentials in the right deltoid, brachioradialis, wrist and finger flexors and extensors, medial portion of the latissimus dorsi and all portions of the trapezius as the backswing started. At this time, there is a second burst in the left anterior deltoid and increased activity in the middle portion of the left deltoid, biceps, brachioradialis, and while the potentials are less than during the toss of the ball, considerable activity is still evident in the middle and lower portions of the left trapezius.

The activity in the right biceps during the backswing for the tennis drive is very much less than that during the basketball distance throw in which the arm must be maintained in a somewhat flexed position to hold the ball, but the brachioradialis activity during the drive backswing is greater as is that of the wrist and finger extensors. The right and left trapezius activity appears to be greater during the backswing of the throw than that of the drive.

The right serratus anterior is active earlier in the tennis drive than the throw. The greatest activity of this muscle appears to have taken place at the end of the backswing of the drive and during the forward swing of the arm in the throw. Also in the throw concurrent activity is seen in the left serratus anterior. Apparently greater stabilization of the shoulder girdle was required by the basketball throw than the tennis drive. This same timing of activity of the right and left serratus anterior is obvious in the records of batting and also all three of the activities using the overhand pattern.

As in the throw, the right anterior (and to a lesser degree, middle) deltoid, the biceps, brachioradialis, wrist and finger flexors and extensors, sternocleidomastoid, trapezius, and pectoral muscles were all active during the forward swing of the racket for the drive. The triceps record shows two short bursts of activity, one near the beginning of the forward swing and the other at impact, while in the throw the activity is centered around the point of release but lasts slightly longer than that seen at contact with the tennis ball. The wrist and finger extensor activity is greater for the drive than the throw indicating the stabilization of the wrist against the force of impact. The activity of the flexors is greater for the basketball throw as is that of the lower trapezius. The difference in flexor activity is undoubtedly caused by the need to hold the ball against the lower arm for the throw. The right latissimus dorsi appears to have been more active during the drive until the point of impact. This muscle shows a burst at release on the throw record, but there is no such burst on the record for the drive.

The augmenting activity of the left arm during the forward swing and release of the throw is not seen on the records for the tennis drive. After tossing the ball for the drive the left arm was much less active than was the case during the basketball throw.

The muscular activity in the right extremity during the follow-through for the drive is the same as for the basketball throw except for greater activity of the biceps and brachioradi-

TENNIS DRIVE

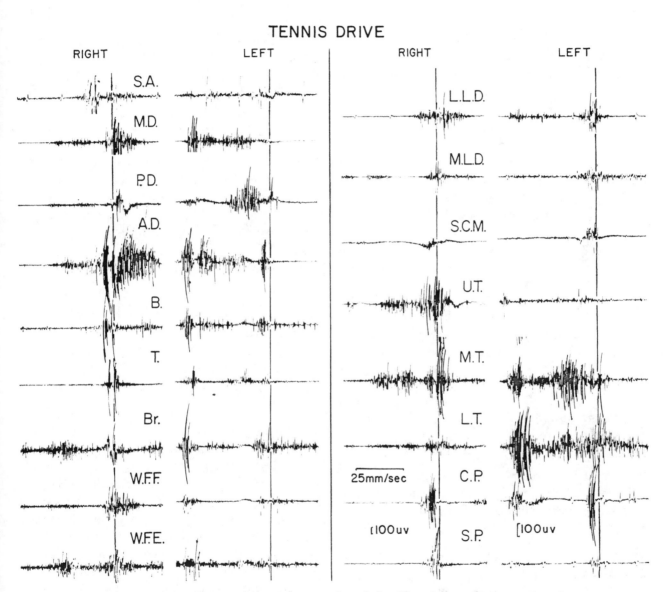

FIGURE 29. TENNIS DRIVE—Activity in muscles of shoulder girdle and upper extremity. See Figure 3 for muscle symbols. Note the increased activity in the left extremity with the toss of the ball.

alis, indicating some bending of the elbow as the racket was closed and brought around toward the left shoulder. Greater activity also occurred in the wrist and finger flexors and extensors to maintain control of the racket.

Back, Abdominal, and Lower Extremity Muscles

Electromyograms of the tennis drive indicate that the timing of electrical potentials in the lower extremity muscles followed the same pattern as for the basketball throw (Fig. 30, p. 63). The magnitude of activity appears to have been somewhat greater for the throw. This is particularly obvious for the thigh muscles and there is more difference between the records of the left thigh muscles than the right.

The records for the sacrospinalis muscles are almost identical for the two activities. However, there is a great difference in the abdominal muscular activity. The basketball throw required a great deal more activity of both the rectus abdominis and the external obliques on the left side of the body than did the tennis drive.

A difference in trunk rotation during the tennis drive and the basketball throw was noted. Although the subject had rotated her trunk forward (facing the direction of the throw) considerably before she released the basketball, her trunk faced diagonally right at impact with the tennis ball. This may account for the greater potentials in the bilateral trapezius, abdominals, and thigh muscles during the throw. Apparently, the momentum of the long arm and racket lever, rather than muscular action, was effective in producing much of the forward rotation during the drive. The difference suggests the possibility that the tennis drive may be a more controlled movement with less explosive force than either the throw or batting.

BATTING

To avoid breakage in the laboratory, a tennis ball was substituted for a softball in batting and a relatively easy pitch was delivered from a distance of approximately eighteen to twenty feet. Because of the short distance, the subject held the bat back rather than swinging it backward in time with the pitch (Fig. 31). However, she did increase the backswing further before starting the forward swing. In spite of the fact that two hands were used on the bat, many similarities in the muscular activity during performance of this skill and the basketball throw and tennis drive are apparent.

Shoulder Girdle and Upper Extremity Muscles
Preparatory Stance

Because the bat was held in the backswing position, activity is seen in the right serratus anterior, bilateral anterior deltoid, biceps, brachioradialis, trapezius, and pectoralis major, and slight activity is apparent in all of the other muscles sampled (Fig. 32, p. 65). The wrist and finger extensors were more active than the flexors. The right wrist and finger flexors and upper trapezius were more active than the left. The difference in microvolts used for the recording of the two extremities (see "uv," Fig. 32) makes it appear that the left biceps, middle and lower trapezius, and wrist and finger extensors were more active than the right. However, only in the case of the lower trapezius does this prove to be the case.

The Swing

As would be anticipated, the burst of activity indicating the backswing of the basketball throw and the tennis drive are not as obvious on the batting record. An increase in backswing immediately prior to the forward swing is indicated by bursts of activity in the right upper and middle trapezius and sternocleidomastoid and the left anterior deltoid and serratus anterior muscles. The timing of potentials for muscles of the right extremity and shoulder girdle is almost identical to that for the basketball throw and is very similar to the tennis drive. When the throw and batting records are superimposed, the only differences in the right muscles that are apparent during the forward swing and follow-through are found in the records of the anterior deltoid, biceps, and brachioradialis activity. The biceps and brachioradialis are

TENNIS DRIVE

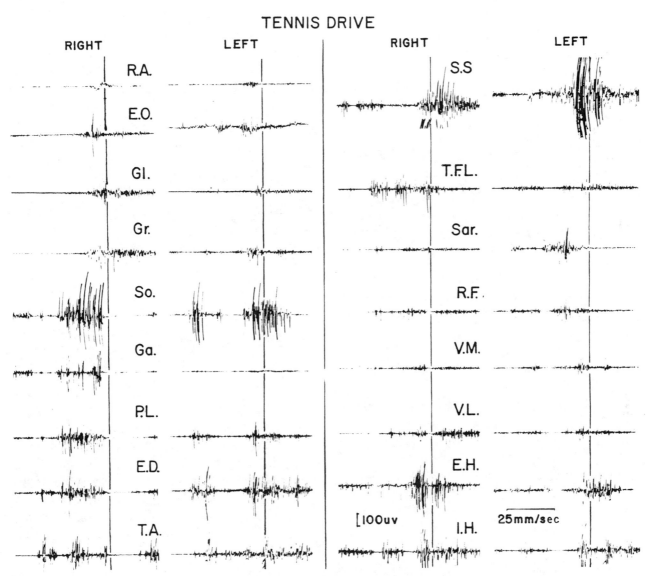

FIGURE 30. TENNIS DRIVE—Activity in muscles of back, abdomen, and lower extremity. See Figure 4 for muscle symbols. Although somewhat less in magnitude, the pattern of activity is very similar to that of the basketball throw (Fig. 27).

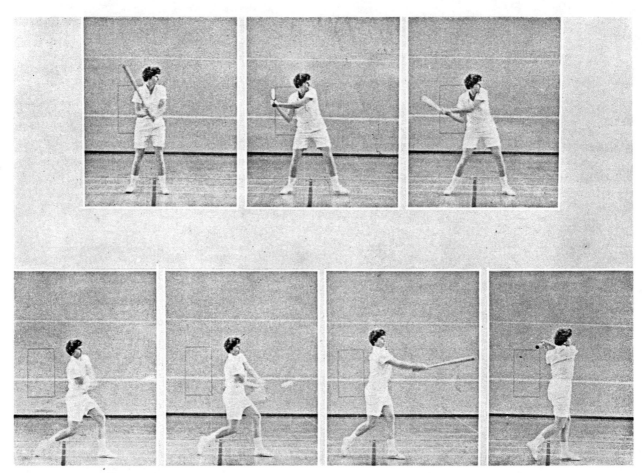

FIGURE 31. BATTING—Frames from motion pictures of subject's performance.

BATTING

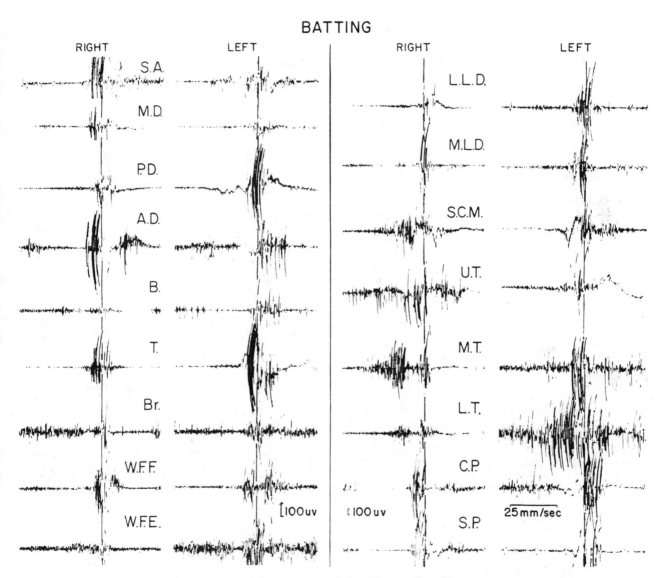

FIGURE 32. BATTING—Activity in muscles of shoulder girdle and upper extremity. See Figure 3 for muscle symbols. Since this is a two-handed activity, the greatest variations from the other two sidearm activities are noticed in the left extremity records.

much less active during the forward swing of the bat than of the basketball. This would be anticipated since the holding of the ball required maintaining some bend in the elbow as the arm was swung through while the batting movement involved extension of the arms. The anterior deltoid is less active during the early part of the follow-through in batting than in either the basketball throw or tennis drive. The same concurrent activity of the right and left serratus anterior, which is seen in the basketball throw but not in the tennis drive, can again be noted in the batting record.

Since the left hand was on the bat, more differences in muscular activity during the performance of the three skills are apparent in the records of the left extremity. Obvious differences are seen in the electromyograms of the biceps, brachioradialis, and triceps muscles. While in the basketball throw and tennis drive the left arm was retracted (posterior deltoid, latissimus dorsi) and flexed at the elbow (brachioradialis, biceps) to balance the forward swing of the right arm, in batting the left elbow was forcefully extended at this time as evidenced by the strong burst of activity in the triceps during the forward swing of the bat while much less activity is seen in the records of the biceps and brachioradialis. The latter two muscles are more active during the follow-through for batting than the other two activities.

The difference between one-handed and two-handed skills is most obvious in the action of the anterior deltoid and the pectoralis major muscles. The records of the right anterior deltoid and pectoralis muscles show large bursts of activity during the forward swing to impact and then these same muscles of the left side of the body burst in the follow-through. This pattern is not seen in the records of the basketball throw or the tennis drive. During batting, the right wrist and finger flexors and left wrist and finger flexors and extensors are active during the forward swing and follow-through. This activity of the left muscles during follow-through is not required by the other two skills since the left hand is not involved in gripping an instru-

ment. Activity is not apparent in either left or right wrist and finger flexors during the follow-through of the throw.

Apparently the subject did not rotate the shoulder girdle as far in batting as during the basketball throw. This is indicated by the lesser activity in the left posterior deltoid, latissimus dorsi, and middle trapezius. This is also true of the tennis drive.

In comparing the left extremity muscles during the three skills, one is impressed with the degree of activity in the so-called "non-participating" extremity during the basketball throw. This activity is somewhat comparable to that evoked during batting which required the active participation of this extremity. The activity in the "non-participating" arm during the tennis drive is considerably less.

Comparison of the batting records with those for golf, another two-handed activity (Fig. 35, p. 70) shows some similarities. However, since the bat was back at the start in batting, this portion of the records cannot be compared and the muscles acting to cause motion in the horizontal plane are more active during the batting swing.

Back, Abdominal, and Lower Extremity Muscles

Preparatory Stance

The fact that the subject started with the bat back is again apparent in the records of the muscular activity in the lower extremities (Fig. 33, p. 67). The potentials (at the extreme left of the record) in the right gracilis, soleus, gastrocnemius, peroneus longus, toe extensors, and tibialis anterior, and the lack of activity in these muscles of the left extremity, indicate that the subject's weight was supported more on the right foot. The activity in the muscles of the leg acting on the foot seems to be erratic, suggesting that the subject may have been adjusting the body in anticipation of the pitch. This is the only activity for which the subject did not control completely the time of the start of the movement.

BATTING

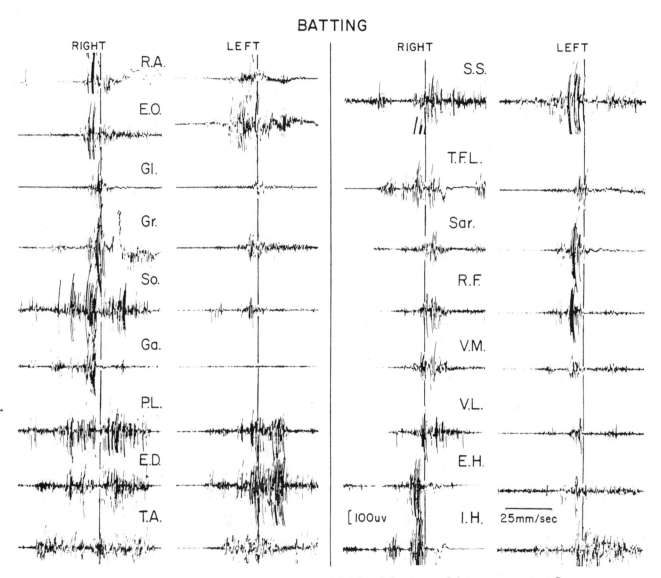

FIGURE 33. BATTING—Activity in muscles of back, abdomen, and lower extremity. See Figure 4 for muscle symbols. Note similarity of activity patterns to those of the basketball throw (Fig. 27). This was the only activity studied for which the subject did not have complete control of the timing since it depended on the delivery of a pitched ball. Since the pitching distance was short the subject held her bat back in anticipation of the pitch. However, she did increase the back swing before swinging forward.

The Swing

The muscle function during backswing differs from that for the basketball throw and tennis drive since the subject started in a backswing position for batting. The increase in the back-swing immediately before the start of the for-ward swing seems to be indicated by small bursts of activity in the right tensor fasciae latae and gracilis and the left peroneus longus and toe extensors which are not obvious on the records of the throw and drive. The right and left soleus and the right gastrocnemius show activity at this time on the records of all three skills.

The muscle function during the forward swing is, in general, the same as for the tennis drive and the basketball throw. In batting, the gracilis and tibialis anterior are active through impact instead of fading just before, as in both the drive and basketball throw.

The outstanding differences are seen in the records taken during the follow-through. The subject kept her right toes on the floor in bat-ting rather than holding the right extremity extended backward as in the throw. There-fore, considerable activity during early follow-through, not seen in either the throw or drive record, is seen in the right soleus, peroneus longus, toe extensors, tibialis anterior, sartorius, rectus femoris, and vastus muscles, and much less is apparent in the right hamstrings. There is less activity in the left gluteus, soleus, quad-riceps, and external hamstrings during the bat-ting than the throw follow-through, and more in the left peroneus longus and toe extensors than in the follow-through of the drive.

In batting, as in the basketball throw, the subject rotated her trunk to face the direction of the hit by impact, and as for the throw, a difference between the activity of the abodim-inal muscles during the tennis drive and bat-ting is apparent. As in the basketball throw considerable activity of the left rectus abdomi-nis and both obliques is seen during the forward swing of batting. In addition, the right rectus abdominis was highly involved in the batting motion probably because the two-handed action required greater stabilization of both sides of the body. It is interesting to note that this is seen in the golf record (Fig. 36, p. 72).

GOLF

Shoulder Girdle and Upper Extremity Muscles

Preparatory Stance

Activity is seen in selected muscles of both shoulder girdles and arms prior to the back-swing as the subject stood holding the club with the clubhead resting squarely behind the cotton ball. The right serratus anterior and bi-lateral pectoral muscles were active in holding the shoulders forward (Fig. 35, p. 70). The mi-nor activity occurring in the middle and lower trapezius may have stabilized the shoulders and, with the latissimus dorsi and the back extensors, maintained the trunk in forward flexion. Bilat-eral activity in the biceps and triceps, all very slight, and in the brachioradialis, probably in-dicates a synergistic action in maintaining elbow extension in both extremities. Undoubt-edly, some of the electrical activity in the brach-ioradialis, and perhaps other forearm muscles, can be attributed to reinforcement in anticipa-tion of the swing. The greatest preparatory ac-tivity is seen in the wrist and finger muscles which were involved in the "waggle" of the club. It is interesting to note that at this time there is considerably more activity in the right flexors than extensors while the activity in the left is more balanced.

The Swing

The initiation of the backswing is indicated by increased activity in the left serratus ante-rior which, with the pectoralis major, was in-volved in rotating the shoulder girdle to the right, and in the right middle, and slightly later in the lower trapezius, which undoubtedly con-tributed to retraction of that shoulder. Simul-taneously, increased activity is apparent in the medial portion of the right latissimus dorsi (and to a lesser degree the lateral portion of the bi-

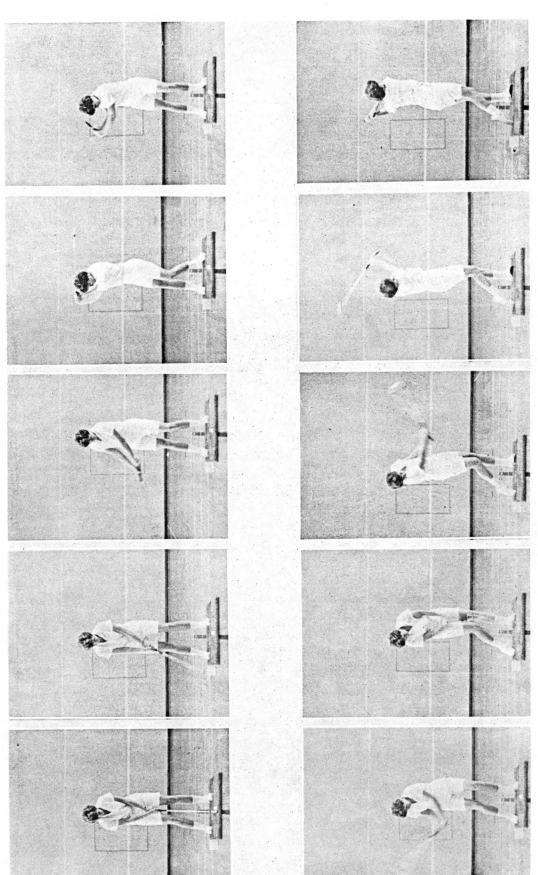

FIGURE 34. GOLF (No. 5 iron)—Frames from motion pictures of subject's performance.

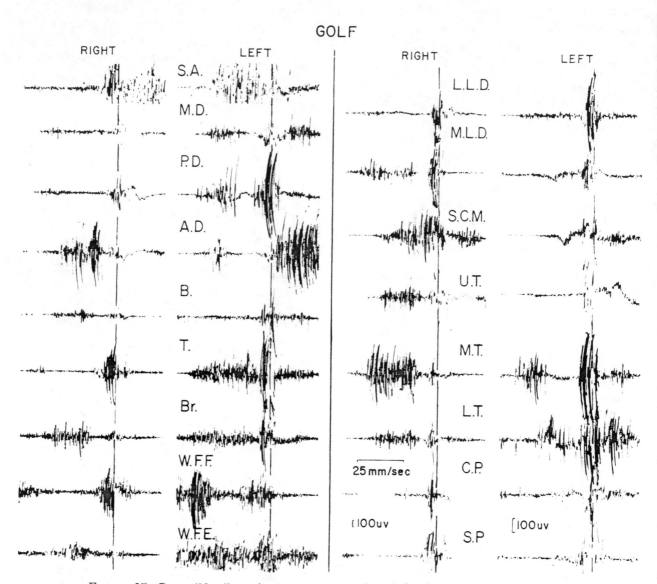

FIGURE 35. GOLF (No. 5 iron)—Activity in muscles of shoulder girdle and upper extremity. See Figure 3 for muscle symbols. A cotton ball rather than a standard golf ball, was used.

lateral muscles), the sacrospinalis and the left external oblique indicating the rotation of the trunk. Actually, there appears to be a very slight reduction of activity in the right sacrospinalis at the exact moment that the above muscles increase in activity, but it then increases again immediately (see later discussion of trunk and leg muscles). Subsequently, increased activity in the right sternocleidomastoid which crescendos at the top of the backswing must indicate the involvement of this muscle in resisting the tendency for the head to follow the rotation of the shoulder girdle and, with the upper trapezius, it may have assisted in maintaining the head in forward flexion so that the subject could look at the ball.

The activity in many arm muscles increases at the same time, indicating that the arms and shoulder girdle performed as a total unit. Activity increases in all three portions of the right deltoid which were probably involved in rotation and very slight abduction of this arm. This is immediately followed by increased activity of the right biceps and brachioradialis and a decrease in activity of the triceps, indicating flexion of the elbow. There is also a decrease of wrist and finger flexors and later an increase in the activity of the wrist and finger extensors. Further increased activity in the right anterior deltoid may indicate that this muscle was stabilizing the arm in relation to the trunk.

During the backswing, the left upper extremity moved diagonally upward across the front of the rotating body. Increased activity in the left serratus anterior is followed immediately by increased activity in the middle trapezius and the three sections of the deltoid, and indicates the beginning of the movement of that shoulder. As the backswing progressed, a greater increase in activity of the serratus anterior indicates its syngeristic action with the middle trapezius, to elevate that shoulder. The activity of the left middle trapezius decreases markedly toward the middle of the backswing at the time when activity in the lower portion increases suggesting that this muscle assists in further elevation. The three portions of the deltoid abducted the arm, the anterior portion, and the biceps contributing to diagonal flexion while the other two portions of the deltoid may have acted to guide and, with the above mentioned muscles, elevate the arm. The increased activity in the left triceps without doubt indicates its involvement in maintaining the elbow in a relatively extended position and the action seen in the biceps and brachioradialis indicates a synergistic action to prevent overextension and to stabilize and guide the forearm and hand. The left wrist and finger flexors show a considerable increase in activity at the beginning of the backswing and then their activity diminishes as the extensors increase, but they increase again and extensors decrease slightly as the top of the backswing is approached.

The top of the backswing, as the club dropped approximately to a horizontal position behind the head, is evidenced by a decrease in electrical activity in the muscles acting on the shoulder girdle with the exception of the left serratus anterior. At this time an increase in activity (which is the very beginning of the crescendo during the forward swing) is seen in the right triceps and wrist and finger flexors, no doubt to check the backward action of the arms and the wrist cock. It may be that the triceps was important in maintaining the adducted position of the upper arm. The posterior deltoid and wrist and finger extensors also seem to have participated in this checking action.

During the forward swing of the club to the point of contact with the ball, bursts of electrical activity are seen in all muscle groups sampled. However, the magnitude of action potentials varies greatly among the various muscles. The right medial and lateral latissimus dorsi and serratus anterior; the left posterior deltoid, lateral latissimus dorsi, middle and lower trapezius; and the bilateral pectorals are extremely active during the forward swing. The head position was maintained by continued activity of the right sternocleidomastoid muscle and increased activity of the left. The activity in the bilateral upper trapezius indicates retraction of the head, which may have reinforced

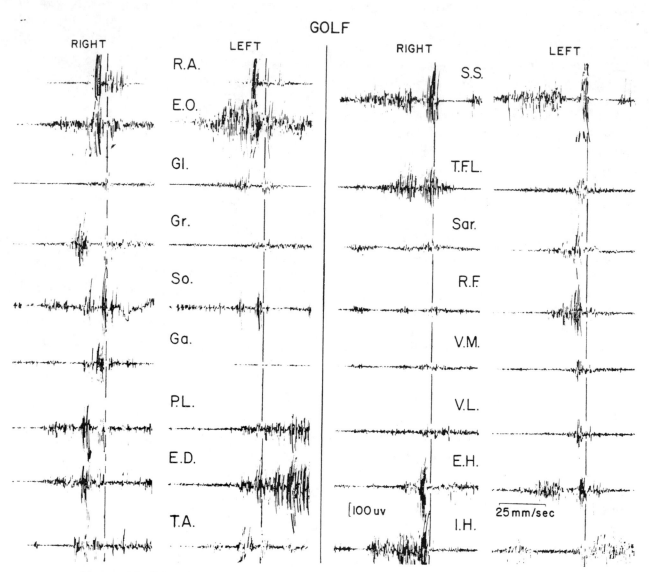

FIGURE 36. GOLF (No. 5 iron)—Activity in muscles of back, abdomen, and lower extremity. See Figure 4 for muscle symbols. The transference of weight to the right on backswing, to equal distribution during forward swing and then to the left is clearly evident in the magnitude of electrical activity in the records of the two extremities.

extensor tonus of the lower extremity. The activity in both triceps crescendos to assure extension of the elbows as the club approached the ball. At the point of impact, as the club was snapped through vigorously, the right wrist and finger flexors and the left extensors are seen to be extremely active.

The shift in pattern of muscle activity from the backswing to the forward swing and follow-through is seen in the changes in magnitude of action potentials in the serratus anterior and middle trapezius. Greater activity is seen in the left serratus anterior and the right middle trapezius as the shoulder girdle was rotated to the right, and in the right serratus anterior and the left middle trapezius as it rotated left. Another shift of pattern is seen in the anterior deltoid muscles; the right acts during the backswing and the left during the follow-through. The relatively small amount of activity in these two muscles during the forward swing, to the point of contact, suggests that after the elbows are extended the shoulder girdle and arms move as a unit. There does not appear to be any indication that one extremity initiates movement and the other follows, but rather the muscle action of the two arms appears to be unified.

During the follow-through, as gravity aided in checking the momentum of the swing, the majority of the muscles sampled show a diminution of activity. Only the right serratus anterior, the left anterior deltoid, and the left lower trapezius show an extreme amount of activity. The left posterior deltoid is extremely active at the beginning of the follow-through and then becomes much less active as the middle deltoid increases its activity. At this same time, the activity of the left middle trapezius also increases somewhat. The left middle and posterior deltoids were probably involved in maintaining the arm in abduction while the left middle and the lower trapezius with the serratus anterior and clavicular portion of the pectoralis elevated the acromion process. Activity of the triceps, biceps, and brachioradialis is seen in both arms, probably indicating that, as the arms were bending, the triceps was checking the momen-

tum. Both wrist and finger flexors and extensors show some activity in both extremities, but the right flexors and left extensors are more active. The action in the sternocleidomastoid, and to a lesser degree in the upper trapezius muscles, probably indicates the turn of the head to follow the ball after the hit. After a short period of maintaining the follow-through posture, the trunk was derotated and the arms with the club were dropped to a position in front of the body.

Back, Abdominal, and Lower Extremity Muscles

Preparatory Stance

As noted earlier, the sacrospinalis muscles with the shoulder girdle muscles appear to have been supporting the flexed trunk against the pull of gravity as the subject assumed her preparatory stance. With the exception of the sartorius, tibialis anterior, and left gastrocnemius,* some activity, although in some cases extremely minor, is seen in all leg and thigh muscles as the subject addressed the ball (Fig. 36, p. 72). Because of the flexed position of the body, the thigh muscles probably were acting to stabilize the knees and help maintain flexion at the hips.

The Swing

During the backswing, considerable activity is seen in the bilateral sacrospinalis and external oblique muscles. The sacrospinalis and left external obliques were probably involved in rotating the body to the right while both may have been stabilizing the pelvis and preventing trunk extension. There are simultaneous bursts of action potentials in the right tensor fasciae latae, sartorius, and quadriceps, no doubt to stabilize the extended right knee. Immediate balance of the weight on the right extremity is indicated by increased activity of the right hamstrings, gastrocnemius, soleus, peroneus longus, and toe extensors. The right gracilis, tensor fasciae latae, and internal hamstring muscles were probably involved in maintaining the thigh in adduction and internal rotation as the rotary forces of the pelvis were resisted.

---

*Left gastrocnemius electrodes apparently had been loosened (see explanation, p. 7).

The rotation of the pelvis to the right drew the left leg into a flexed position at the hip and knee. Even though the knee dropped toward the right extremity, the left thigh was abducted and externally rotated on the pelvis and the activity seen in the left gluteus maximus, tensor fasciae latae, sartorius, and external hamstring no doubt can be attributed to this action. During the last part of the backswing, when the left knee was further flexed, the activity in the external hamstrings diminishes and that of the rectus femoris starts to increase, no doubt indicating the straightening of the hip in preparation for the weight shift to the left leg. Action is also seen in the left soleus, and toward the end of the backswing the activity increases in the peroneus longus, extensor digitorum, and tibialis anterior as these muscles acted from the foot to resist the pull of the rotary forces on the leg.

At the top of the backswing, as the club was dropped to a horizontal position behind the head, considerable bilateral rectus abdominis activity is evident and, at the same time, the electrical activity in the bilateral sacrospinalis decreases. Undoubtedly, the abdominals were involved in resisting momentum forces which would tend to pull the body into extension, and it is possible also that these might have been involved in respiratory action. As the trunk was rotated to the left during the forward swing, activity in the abdominals is seen to diminish and the bilateral sacrospinalis muscles show bursts of activity. The right sacrospinalis begins to burst before the left. After contact with the ball, the abdominals are again active during the follow-through phase as the trunk rotated and extended to the left. Considerable activity is seen in the external obliques throughout the swing with the exception of the time immediately before contact, when the activity appears to diminish greatly. The right external oblique seems to be most active at the top of the backswing and the beginning of the forward swing when it probably was involved in effecting the change from right to left rotation as well as fixing the pelvis, and the rib cage for shoulder action.

As the top of the backswing was approached, bursts of activity are apparent in the right soleus, gastrocnemius, peroneus longus, toe extensors, and tibialis anterior which may have resisted the body rotary forces and, acting from their attachments on the foot, started the transference of weight to the left extremity. Concurrent electrical activity is seen in the left gluteus maximus, soleus, sartorius, and rectus femoris, which probably were involved in extending that thigh and knee. Immediately thereafter, activity increases in the left peroneus longus, toe extensors, tibialis anterior, and slightly later bursts appear in the left sartorius, rectus femoris, and vastus medialis and lateralis, no doubt indicating stabilization of the left extremity for the driving action of the arms. It appears that just before contact the weight was equally distributed since the left leg and thigh muscles continued to be active and renewed bursts of activity are found in the right leg and thigh muscles.

After contact with the ball, the body was rotated to the left and the weight was carried primarily on the extended left extremity. Activity is seen in all left lower extremity muscles, particularly the peroneus longus, extensor digitorum longus, and internal hamstrings. The right hip and knee were flexed and activity to maintain the position is seen in all of the right thigh muscles. Evidence of the dropping inward of the flexed right knee and the lifting of the right heel is seen in the activity of the right gracilis, soleus, gastrocnemius, peroneus longus, extensor digitorum longus, and tibialis anterior.

The position of the body at the top of the backswing is similar to that at the end of the follow-through, but reversed from right to left. Therefore, distinct reversals in muscle patterns might be anticipated and, in some instances, this is found. For the most part, however, these muscle patterns are masked by the fact that, during the backswing, the activity was more deliberate and controlled than during the follow-through phase. The activity at the top of the backswing, which has a braking component as well as a reversal action, is not seen as distinctly at the end of the follow-through phase. There is no activity at the end of the follow-through comparable to the build-up of activity just preceding the top of the back-swing as evident in the records of the left gluteus maximus, sartorius, rectus femoris, and right gracilis and tensor fasciae latae. Transfer of weight is most obvious in the action of the internal hamstrings, peroneus longus, and toe extensors, as the right muscles are most active during the backswing and the left during the follow-through phase. Body rotation to the right elicits greater magnitude of electrical activity in the left external and right internal hamstrings. The reverse is evident during rotation to the left. Increased activity in the bilateral sacrospinalis seen at the extreme right of the record suggests the end of the follow-through phase and the beginning of return to normal standing position.

Chapter VII

Comparison of the Three Throws

A COMPARISON of the electromyograms for the three throws, underhand, overhand, and sidearm (basketball), indicates that the muscular activity in the lower extremities is more similar than might be anticipated (Figs. 4, 17, and 27).

When a transparency of the electromyograms of the overhand throw was superimposed on the record of the underhand throw, it was found that, in general, the patterns of activity are the same. The underhand throw record shows more activity in the left gracilis, soleus, and external hamstrings, and the right tensor fasciae latae, sartorius, rectus femoris, and vastus medialis, although the *timing* for the last three is identical for the two throws. The right gracilis has a larger short burst of activity during the overhand throw, but is active longer in the underhand throw. The activity of the internal hamstring muscles is somewhat different for the two throws. The greater body rotation used in the overhand throw is apparent in the activity of the left rectus abdominis and external oblique muscles.

Except for slightly more activity in the right vastus medialis during the forward swing and in the left soleus during the follow-through (very comparable to the underhand throw), the record for the back, abdominal, and lower extremity muscles during the basketball throw is identical to that for the overhand throw. In view of the similarities between the various striking and throwing activities discussed earlier, it would seem that there may be a general pattern of muscle function which is used with slight adjustments when the body wishes to throw or strike with considerable force.

Although many of the muscles in the shoulder girdle and upper extremity function in the same way during the three throws, these electromyograms indicate many more differences than do those for the lower extremities (Figs. 3, 15, and 26).

Chapter VIII

One-Foot Jump

SEVERAL skills require the conversion of forward momentum to upward momentum in projecting the body into the air. The two included in this study are the basketball lay-up and the volleyball spike. It is interesting to note that while the purposes of the two skills require different muscle function in the upper extremities, that of the lower extremities is almost identical.

VOLLEYBALL SPIKE

Because of the limitations of the ceiling of the laboratory, an operator held a standard volleyball on her palm 8½ feet from the floor. The subject made her normal two step approach, jumping from the left foot to strike the ball (Fig. 37).

Shoulder Girdle and Upper Extremity Muscles

Preparatory Stance

No activity was evident in the arm and forearm muscles at this time. There was minor activity in the left anterior and posterior deltoid and middle trapezius, probably postural or anticipatory in nature (Fig. 38, p. 79).

The Spike

The first swing phase of the right foot in approach to the spike is accompanied by bursts of electrical activity in the right triceps to retract that arm, and left biceps, brachioradialis, and middle deltoid to forward flex the left. No weight in the form of a racket or ball was held in the upper extremities, thus the reciprocal action of the arms can be clearly differentiated. Activity in the right triceps is followed immediately by bursts of activity in all portions of the deltoids to maintain slight abduction, the latissimus dorsi to retract the arm, and the serratus anterior and middle and lower trapezius to stabilize the shoulder girdle.

The second step, left foot forward, can be seen in the reversal of action in the muscles of the upper extremity. As the right triceps diminishes, the right anterior deltoid, biceps, and brachioradialis increase in action. Simultaneously, there is a diminution in the left biceps, brachioradialis, and wrist and finger extensors as action increases in the triceps, latissimus dorsi, and deltoids. Muscles of the upper extremity which were active have a tendency to show two bursts of activity; one at the beginning and one at the end of the step. It may be that the first burst indicates the checking action of the backward swing and the beginning of the forward action, while the second burst of activity may mark the end of the forward swing of the arm. Between the two bursts of activity in the right biceps and brachioradialis, there is a burst of activity in the triceps possibly indicating an extension of the elbow as the arm was swung forward.

A burst of activity in the right sternocleidomastoid, simultaneous with the first burst in the anterior deltoid, biceps, and brachioradialis suggests that this muscle may have been stabilizing the shoulder. It may also have acted to maintain the head in a position facing the ball. This

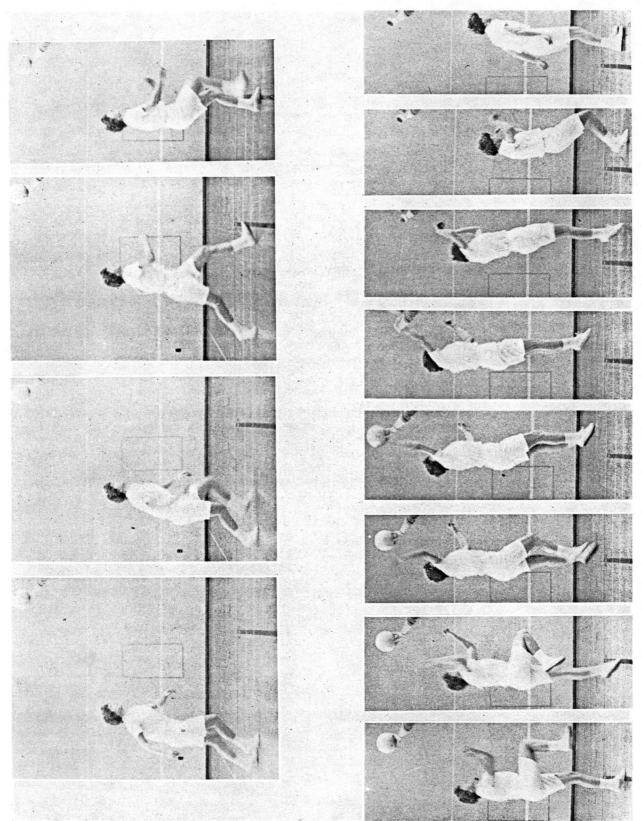

Figure 37. Volleyball Spike—Frames from motion pictures of subject's performance.

VOLLEYBALL SPIKE

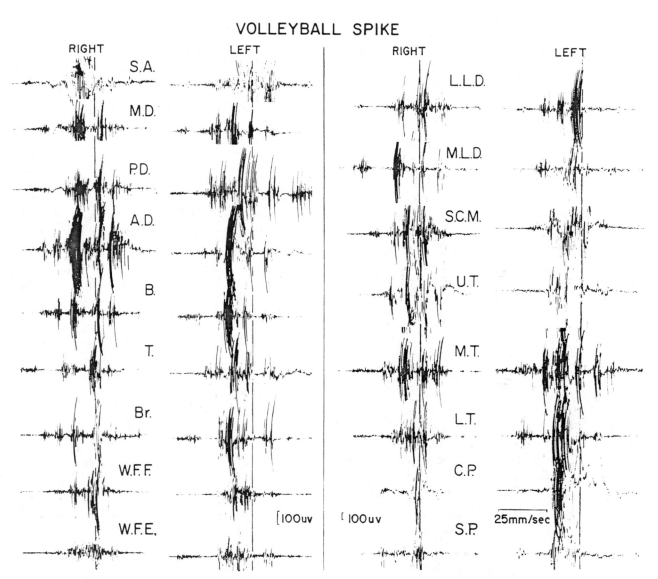

FIGURE 38. VOLLEYBALL SPIKE—Activity in muscles of shoulder girdle and upper extremity. See Figure 3 for muscle symbols.

burst is followed immediately by increased action in the left sternocleidomastoid and bilateral upper trapezius muscles as they tilted the head backward in preparation for the spike. In timing with the second burst of activity in the biceps, brachioradialis and anterior deltoid, the middle deltoid, pectoralis major, and middle trapezius show an increase in magnitude, possibly to stabilize the shoulder girdle in preparation for the forward and upward movement of the upper extremity and body.

The left upper extremity and shoulder girdle reflect the forward progress and vertical jump. Bursts of activity in the latissimus dorsi, middle and anterior deltoid, biceps, brachioradialis, and wrist and finger flexors occur at the same time, while action, either preceding or following, is seen in the posterior deltoid, triceps, and wrist and finger extensors. The left middle and lower trapezius, serratus anterior, and pectoralis major are active at the end of the first step and into the second step.

The contribution of the upper extremities to the force of the jump is apparent in the tremendous bursts of activity in selected muscles of the shoulder girdle and upper extremities which appear to precede slightly or coincide with the extension of the left lower extremity. Bursts in both the right and left anterior deltoids, biceps, brachioradialis, and the medial portion of the right latissimus dorsi slightly precede the jump while those of most of the other muscles coincide with the take-off. From the beginning of the upward movement until impact, there are variable magnitudes of electrical activity in most of the muscles. The exceptions are the bilateral serratus anterior and the wrist and finger extensor muscles, which seem to maintain their activity throughout the movement. Bilateral action of the sternocleidomastoid muscles, which also appears to be fairly consistent, probably indicates involvement with the upper trapezius in the backward tilt of the head. These muscles may also have acted to stabilize the shoulder girdle.

Just before contact, the arm was extended to maximum height and the trunk, which had been in a slightly forward position prior to the thrusting of the body into the air, was extended to its maximum. Muscles of the right extremity which appear to have been most active at impact are the anterior deltoid, triceps, wrist and finger flexors, lateral portion of the latissimus dorsi, sternocleidomastoid, pectoralis major, and trapezius muscles. The wrist and finger extensor activity was probably involved in wrist stabilization. The biceps and brachioradialis begin to act at impact possibly to brake the extension action of the elbow and also to protect it against the force of impact. Immediately after contact, there appears to be a braking action of the muscles, primarily the three portions of the deltoid, and the wrist and finger muscles. Both portions of the right latissimus dorsi were active in the forceful pull of the arm from maximum extension to a flexed position. The upper trapezius, and probably the middle and lower, contributed to elevation of the shoulder. The middle and lower portions of this muscle were undoubtedly active as stabilizers. At contact, activity in the right serratus anterior diminishes somewhat and then continues, to a lesser degree, into the follow-through stage.

Immediately prior to and through contact, the left extremity was in forward flexion and abducted with the elbow flexed. There is increased activity in the three portions of the deltoid muscles. The timing of activity in the biceps, brachioradialis, and wrist and finger extensors is similar while that in the triceps and wrist and finger flexors shows a comparable pattern. Activity in these muscles ceases or diminishes prior to the impact.

Increased activity is obvious in the left latissimus dorsi muscle, which may have been concerned with activity of the arm, although a more probable action may have been to extend the trunk and support it as the right arm was whipped forward. The left middle and lower trapezius, particularly the middle, show a burst of activity while the activity in the lower trapezius continues at a lesser degree of magnitude. Activity in the left pectoralis major diminishes at contact. Muscles acting on the shoulder girdle were probably concerned with supporting the trunk and rib cage as the right arm was whipped forward. The left serratus anterior is active throughout the period and into the follow-through.

In the follow-through phase, the three portions of the right deltoid, the biceps, and triceps probably were involved in braking the forward action of the arm. A burst of activity in both right and left posterior and anterior deltoids and biceps occurs at the time the weight was taken on the two feet. This timing is also noted in the burst of activity in the brachioradialis on the left side. It is also evident in the right latissimus dorsi and the upper, middle, and lower trapezius of both sides. Activity diminishes in all muscles after the weight was taken on both extremities. Minor activity continues to occur in the left posterior deltoid and the middle trapezius, probably because of postural adjustment.

Back, Abdominal, and Lower Extremity Muscles

Preparatory Stance

During this period, activity is most noticeable (extreme left of the illustration) in the thigh muscles (Fig. 39, p. 82). Although the leg muscles appear to be relatively quiet, with the exception of the right toe extensors and tibialis anterior, sporadic activity is evident in the right soleus, gastrocnemius, peroneus longus, and in the left soleus prior to preparation for the first step. Activity in the thigh and sacrospinalis muscles suggests that the subject was in a slight crouch position with hips and knees flexed.

The Spike

The movement of the right foot forward is indicated by small short bursts in the right soleus, followed by the gastrocnemius, tibialis anterior, internal hamstrings, and tensor fasciae latae. The supporting left extremity shows increased activity in the soleus, peroneus longus, toe extensors, tibialis anterior, tensor fasciae latae, and a gradual diminution of activity in the quadriceps muscles. The hamstrings are active about the middle of the supporting phase and again at the beginning of the left swinging phase. The right sartorius and rectus femoris increase in activity momentarily at the end of the step and possibly the beginning of the next.

As the weight was transferred to the right flexed extremity, there is a large burst of activity in the left soleus and lesser bursts in the left toe extensors and hamstrings. This is followed by a small burst in the tibialis anterior, gracilis, sartorius, rectus femoris, and vastus medialis (slight). Activity diminishes slightly in the right tibialis anterior and increases in the other muscles of the leg acting on the foot. Increased activity also occurred in the thigh muscles to maintain the flexed hip and knee. At this time, activity increases somewhat in the bilateral external obliques and sacrospinalis muscles, followed immediately by slightly increased activity in the rectus abdominis. These muscles may have acted to support the pelvis and the rib cage and to prepare for the upward movement of the trunk in the jump.

As the weight was taken on the left foot in preparation for the vertical jump, bursts of activity occur in the left hamstrings, gracilis, and soleus, followed immediately by bursts in all muscles of this leg and thigh. This suggests the above mentioned muscles may have acted to flex the thigh briefly before the extremity was extended by all muscles. A pause in the activity of the right soleus, gastrocnemius, peroneus longus, toe extensors, sartorius, vastus medialis, vastus lateralis, and external hamstrings occurs at the same time the left extremity muscles acted to initiate the jump. Renewed bursts in these muscles, with the continued activity in the gracilis, tibialis anterior, tensor fasciae latae, rectus femoris, and internal hamstrings indicate the strong flexion of the hip and knee as the lift of the right knee added force to the jump.

Increased activity in the left sacrospinalis and bilateral external oblique muscles, and to a lesser degree the right sacrospinalis and right and left rectus abdominis, slightly precedes the jump. The abdominals probably acted to stabilize the rib cage and pelvis and prevent over-

VOLLEYBALL SPIKE

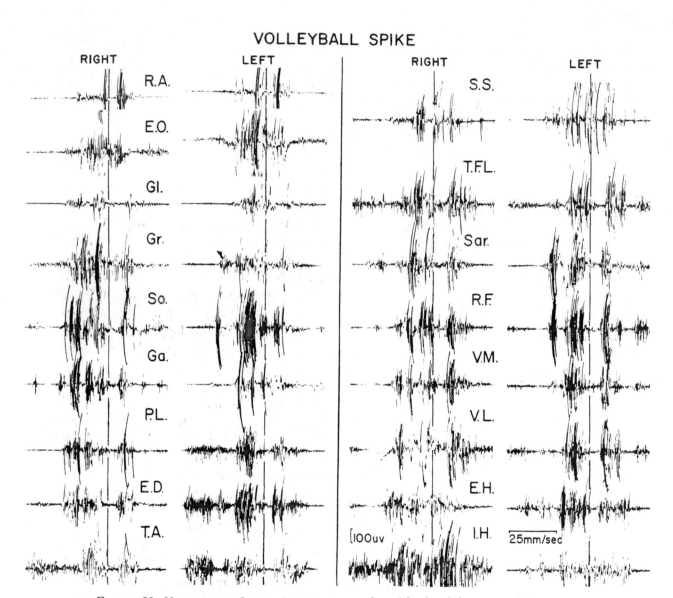

FIGURE 39. VOLLEYBALL SPIKE—Activity in muscles of back, abdomen, and lower extremity. See Figure 4 for muscle symbols.

extension of the trunk. As the right arm was swung upward and forward for the impact, the external obliques may have contributed to stabilization and then flexion of the trunk. The sacrospinalis muscles may have functioned as extensors of the spine. The left muscle probably contributed to the extensor thrust of the lower extremity by action on the pelvis.

There is an instantaneous pause or cessation of activity in the right leg muscles shortly before the impact. At this time, there is activity in the right thigh muscles as they were involved, with gravity, in extending the hip and knee. The left extremity muscles show a lesser degree of activity at contact.

The abdominals burst immediately prior to contact, probably to forward flex the trunk as the right extremity was brought forward to hit the ball. Thereafter, the sacrospinalis was active to prevent further forward flexion. Another burst of activity in the bilateral rectus abdominis and sacrospinalis occurs in the follow-through as the subject landed after the jump. The external obliques show continued activity from contact to recovery of balance.

Landing and recovery of balance after the jump is obvious by bursts of activity in most of the muscles. A second burst or continued activity in the thigh muscles and selected muscles of the legs indicates that as the subject landed the knees flexed and then were extended. Diminution of activity in all muscles indicates recovery of balance; apparently she moved her left leg, as there was increased activity in the thigh muscles after recovery.

BASKETBALL LAY-UP

A basketball hoop was not available. However, the subject attempted to hit a simulated target on the ceiling of the laboratory. She bounced the ball as she stepped onto her right foot and then stepped left and took her jump for the lay-up (Fig. 40). In most instances she caught the ball after the lay-up and this is reflected in the muscle action after the follow-through.

Shoulder Girdle and Upper Extremity Muscles

Preparatory Stance

Minor activity is evident in bilateral biceps, brachioradialis, wrist and finger flexors and extensors, and the left triceps as the subject supported the ball in two hands (Fig. 41, p. 85). Activity in the left serratus anterior, posterior deltoid, and middle trapezius suggests that the ball was held to the right of the subject.

The Lay-up

At the same time that the right foot began to swing forward, preparation for the bounce of the ball is seen in the increased activity of the right serratus anterior, middle and anterior deltoid, triceps (slight), and wrist and finger flexors, followed immediately by small bursts in the right middle and anterior deltoid, biceps, and brachioradialis. This is followed by activity in the serratus anterior and large bursts in the anterior deltoid, triceps, and wrist and finger extensors, followed by flexors as the ball was pushed toward the floor. This activity occurs during the first step (right). As the weight was being taken onto the left foot, renewed activity in the serratus anterior and renewed bursts in the anterior deltoid, biceps, brachioradialis, and wrist and finger flexors, together with all sections of the trapezius, indicate that the ball was caught and the lift began.

Activity in the bilateral pectoralis major, serratus anterior, and all portions of the trapezius seem to indicate that the forward and upward movement of the shoulder girdle preceded slightly the upward extension of the upper extremity, thus adding force to the lift of the body. Activity in the latissimus dorsi, along with the trapezius muscles, may have contributed to extension of the trunk. The upper trapezius, with the sternocleidomastoid muscles, controlled the tilt of the head upward.

The beginning movement of the upper extremities upward to lift the ball is indicated by a fourth burst of activity in the right anterior

FIGURE 40. BASKETBALL LAY-UP—Frames from motion pictures of subject's performance.

BASKETBALL LAY-UP

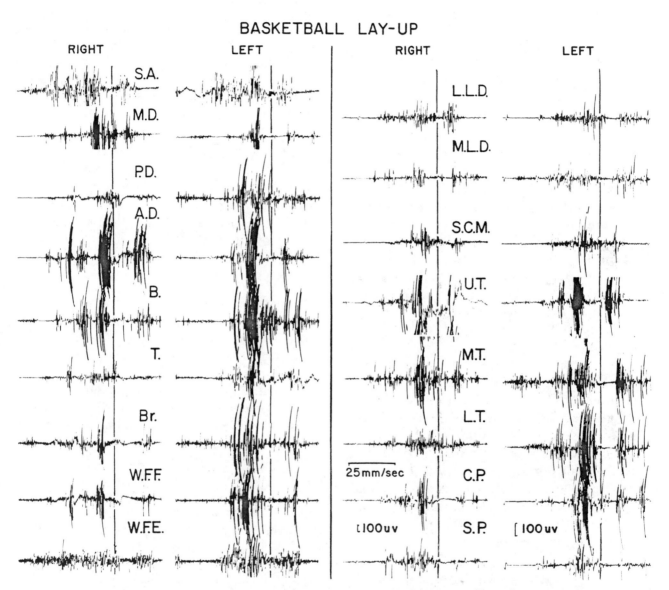

FIGURE 41. BASKETBALL LAY-UP—Activity in muscles of shoulder girdle and upper extremity. See Figure 3 for muscle symbols. Note the similarity in pattern between this illustration and that of the volleyball spike (Fig. 38), despite the fact that she had a ball in this activity.

deltoid and biceps in time with bursts of activity in the left anterior and posterior deltoid, biceps, triceps, brachioradialis, wrist and finger flexors and extensors, followed by the right brachioradialis and wrist and finger flexors. Some activity in the right triceps is apparent also during the lift of the ball. Activity in the right wrist and finger extensors continues throughout the basketball lay-up and into the follow-through.

The muscle action in the left extremity during the step and jump is almost identical to that seen on the record of the volleyball spike. (Fig. 38, p. 79). Some differences during the early part of the action would be anticipated since the left hand was on the basketball. However, it would appear that the left arm was used as effectively in producing upward force to augment the force of the leg extension as when it was not involved with the ball (Figs. 38, 41, pp. 79, 85). The right arm activity is very different for these two skills, although the action of the middle deltoid, upper, and middle trapezius muscles at the time of the jump is seen on both records. Apparently the right arm, which is involved in ball control, cannot be used as effectively in producing upward force as when free of the ball in the spike. The greater freedom of the right arm to function effectively in producing upward force during the spike than during the lay-up is seen in the bursts of activity in the right anterior deltoid, biceps, and brachioradialis, which are on the spike records at the time of the jump, but not on the lay-up electromyograms.

Immediately prior to the release of the ball, the extended body was rotated slightly toward the left so that the right upper extremity was nearer the target. This may be why activity increases in the middle, then in anterior and posterior right deltoids, and diminishes in the right serratus anterior and pectoralis major muscles. The right triceps and wrist and finger extensors continue to act throughout the lay-up while activity in the brachioradialis and wrist and finger flexors diminishes.

Two bursts of activity in the follow-through phase are distinguishable in the left anterior deltoid, biceps, bilateral middle and lower trapezius, and pectoralis major muscles. The first burst occurs at the time the subject recovered balance after the jump (lower extremities, Fig. 42, p. 88). Concurrent activity is seen in the bilateral serratus anterior, middle deltoid, latissimus dorsi, sternocleidomastoid, upper trapezius, right anterior deltoid, left posterior deltoid, and left wrist and finger flexors. The second burst occurs probably as the subject recovered the ball. During this second burst, there is increased activity in the right biceps, left triceps, and bilateral brachioradialis, wrist and finger flexors and right extensors. At this time, there is also activity in the lateral portion of the left latissimus dorsi and bilateral medial portions of the latissimus dorsi muscles, possibly to assist in recovery of balance as well as of the ball.

Back, Abdominal, and Lower Extremity Muscles

Except for more activity during the stance preparatory to the basketball lay-up and less during extension of the right leg just before release, the electromyograms of the lower extremity muscles are identical to those of the volleyball spike (Figs. 39, 42, pp. 82, 88). This would be anticipated since both skills were approached with a step onto the right foot, followed by a step onto the left foot from which a jump was taken, accompanied by the forceful lift of the right knee. Apparently the right leg was extended with more force as the right arm was brought through to strike the ball than when the arm was extended upward for the lay-up. The greater activity of the rectus femoris at this time may indicate its involvement in the forward flexion of the trunk during the spike.

The only other differences which are apparent in these electromyograms involve the abdominal and sacrospinalis muscles. Since the lay-up required an upward extension as opposed to the forceful forward-downward striking motion of the spike, the activity in all abdominal muscles is much less on the lay-up record. This difference is most obvious for the rectus abdominis. As might be expected, there is also less activity in the left sacrospinalis during the upward extension than during the striking movement (period preceding contact or release) and also less in the right sacrospinalis during the follow-through of the lay-up.

BASKETBALL LAY-UP

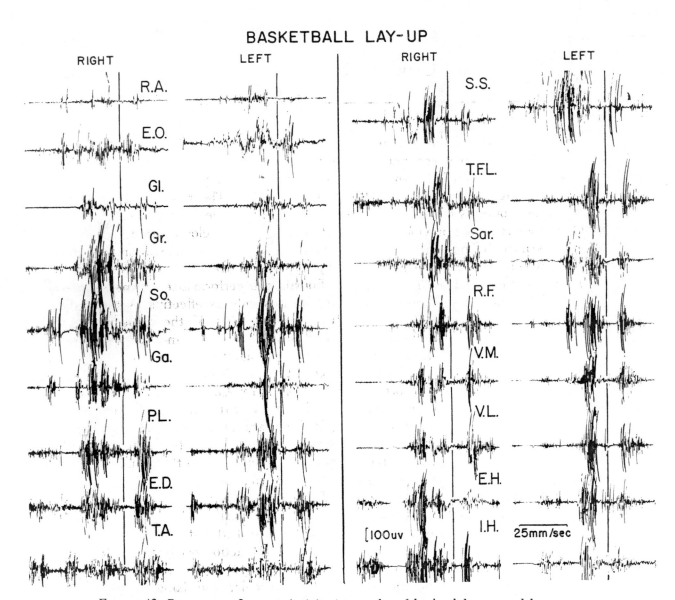

FIGURE 42. BASKETBALL LAY-UP—Activity in muscles of back, abdomen, and lower extremity. See Figure 4 for muscle symbols. Note that this activity pattern is almost identical to that for the volleyball spike (Fig. 39).

Chapter IX

General Observations

In the process of attempting to correlate muscle action patterns with movement patterns during the performance of these thirteen sport skills, several interesting generalizations were deduced. While these concepts may not necessarily be original, they reinforce previous ideas.

First, there appear to be basic patterns of muscular activity which, with minor variations, are seen in various groups of skills. The slight adjustments can be related to differences in specific purposes of the given skills and/or equipment employed. The timing of activity for a given muscle is relatively constant for a group of similar skills. The magnitude of action potentials varies directly with the effort required by the purpose. Patterns of muscular activity for the supporting and swinging phases in those activities requiring steps are not unlike those seen in walking. The electrical activity is greater in the leg muscles and more thigh muscles participate because of the greater force required and the more or less flexed position of the hips and knees during the performance of the various sport skills.

Second, rotary movement is initiated centrally and proceeds peripherally. Rotation of the pelvis, trunk, and shoulder girdle precedes the action of the upper extremity.

Third, the non-participating left upper extremity in single arm activities is non-existent. Organized patterns of electrical activity in the left upper extremity and shoulder girdle are extremely important for stabilization, balance, and reinforcement. In single arm activities, the left extremity is retracted and the elbow flexed as the right extremity is forward flexed and the elbow extended. The role of the contralateral extremity during the performance of unilateral activities warrants closer attention when attempting to diagnose causes of faulty techniques.

Fourth, the performance of one segment of the body is only as effective as the stabilization or positioning of the adjacent segment. Coordination of the hand depends on the strength and agility of the wrist. The performance of the arm is only as good as the control of the shoulder girdle. The nicety of coordinated movement depends on the temporal and spatial pattern of every muscle of the body acting across its respective joint or joints to move the levers through the desired distance in the desired direction.

Fifth, in a coordinated skill as herein presented, the agonist's action does not appear to relax the so-called antagonist muscle. Synergistic or fixing action occurs to guide and control the primary movement. When muscle function is diarticular, the fixing or synergistic action of the muscles performing the opposite movement is extremely important.

Sixth, when the weight is shifted from one lower extremity to the other in a forceful activity, it appears that the body is pushed from the one extremity to the other.

Bibliography

1. ALLEN, C. E. L.: Muscle action potentials used in the study of dynamic anatomy. *Brit J Phys Med*, *11*:66-73, 1948.

2. BASMAJIAN, J. V.: *Muscles Alive—Their Functions Revealed By Electromyography.* Baltimore, Williams and Wilkins, 1962.

3. BIERMAN, W., and YAMSHON, L. J.: Electromyography in kinesiologic evaluations. *Arch Phys Med*, *29*:206-211, 1948.

4. BROER, M. R.: *Efficiency of Human Movement.* Philadelphia, Saunders, 1960, revised edition, 1966.

5. CAMPBELL, E. J. M.: An electromyographic study of the role of the abdominal muscles in breathing. *J Physiol*, *117*:222-233, 1952.

6. CLOSE, J. R.: *Motor Function in the Lower Extremity.* Springfield, Thomas, 1964.

7. Examiner's Manual: *Minnesota Rate of Manipulation Test.* Minneapolis, Educational Test Bureau, Educational Publishers, Inc., 1946.

8. FLOYD, W. F., and SILVER, P. H. S.: Electromyographic study of patterns of activity of the anterior abdominal wall muscles in man. *J Anat*, *84*:132-145, 1950.

9. FLOYD, W. F., and SILVER, P. H. S.: Function of erectores spinae in flexion of the trunk. *Lancet*, *1*:133-134, 1951.

10. FLOYD, W. F., and SILVER, P. H. S.: The function of the erectores spinae muscles in certain movements and postures in man. *J Physiol*, *129*:184-203, 1955.

11. GELLHORN, E.: Patterns of muscular activity in man. *Arch Phys Med*, *28*:568-574, 1947.

12. GROFF, R. A., and HOUTZ, S. J.: *Manual of Diagnosis and Management of Peripheral Nerve Injuries.* Philadelphia, Lippincott, 1945.

13. HELLEBRANDT, F. A., HOUTZ, S. J., PARTRIDGE, M. J., and WALTERS, C. E.: The Chandler Table: Analysis of its rationale in the mobilization of the shoulder joint. *Phys Ther Rev*, *35*:545-556, 1955.

14. HELLEBRANDT, F. A., HOUTZ, S. J., PARTRIDGE, M. J., and WALTERS, C. E.: Tonic neck reflexes in heavy resistance in man. *Amer J Phys Med*, *35*:144-159, 1956.

15. HELLEBRANDT, F. A., and HOUTZ, S. J.: Mechanisms of muscle training in man. *Phys Ther Rev*, *36*:371-383, 1956.

16. HELLEBRANDT, F. A., and HOUTZ, S. J.: Cross education in prosthetic training of the below elbow amputee. *Amer J Phys Med*, *36*:186-211, 1957.

17. HOUTZ, S. J., and FISCHER, F. J.: An analysis of muscle action and joint excursion during exercise on a stationary bicycle. *J Bone Joint Surg*, *41*:123-131, 1959.

18. HOUTZ, S. J., and WALSH, F. P.: Electromyographic analysis of the function of the muscles acting on the ankle during weightbearing with special reference to the triceps surae. *J Bone Joint Surg*, *41*:1481-1469, 1959.

19. HOUTZ, S. J., and FISCHER, F. J.: Function of leg muscles acting on foot as modified by body movements. *J Appl Physiol*, *16*:597-605, 1961.

20. HOUTZ, S. J.: Influence of gravitational forces on function of lower extremity muscles. *J Appl Physiol*, *19*:999-1004, 1964.

21. INMAN, V. T., SAUNDERS, J. B., and ABBOTT, L. C.: Observations on the function of the shoulder joint. *J Bone Joint Surg*, *26A*:1-30, 1944.

22. JOSEPH, J.: *Man's Posture Electromyographic Studies.* Springfield, Thomas, 1960.

23. KITZMAN, ERIC W.: Baseball: Electromyographic study of batting swing. *Res Quart* *35*:166-178, 1964.

24. LONG, C., and BROWN, M. E.: Electromyographic kinesiology of the hand: Muscles moving the long finger. *J Bone Joint Surg, 46A:* 1683-1706, 1964.

25. NAKAMURA, Y., OOTA, Y., and MIWA, N.: Study on the finger moving muscles in man. *Kyushu J Med Sci, 8:*199-298, 1957.

26. PARTRIDGE, M. J., and WALTERS, C. E.: Participation of the abdominal muscles in various movements of the trunk in man. *Phys Ther Rev, 39:*791-800, 1959.

27. PORTNOY, H., and MORIN, F.: Electromyographic study of postural muscles in various positions and movements. *Amer J Physiol, 186:*122-126, 1956.

28. REEDER, T.: Electromyographic study of the latissimus dorsi muscle. *J Amer Phys Ther Ass, 43:*165-172, 1963.

29. SAHA, A. K.: *Theory of Shoulder Mechanism: Descriptive and Applied.* Springfield, Thomas, 1961.

30. SATO, M.: Electromyographical study of skilled movement. *J Faculty of Science,* University of Tokyo, *Section V2:*323-369, 1963.

31. SLATER-HAMMEL, A. T.: Action current study of contraction—movement relationships in golf stroke. *Res Quart 19:*164-177, 1948.

32. SLATER-HAMMEL, A. T.: Action current study of contraction—movement relationships in the tennis stroke. *Res Quart 20:*424-431, 1949.

33. SLAUGHTER, D. R.: Electromyographic studies of arm movements. *Res Quart 30:*326-327, 1959.

34. WHEATLEY, M. D., and JAHNKE, W. D.: Electromyographic study of the superficial thigh and hip muscles in normal individuals. *Arch Phys Med, 32:*508-515, 1951.

35. YAMSHON, L. J., and BIERMAN, W.: Kinesiologic electromyography. II. The trapezius. *Arch Phys Med, 29:*647-651, 1948.

36. YAMSHON, L. J., and BIERMAN, W.: Kinesiologic electromyography. III. The deltoid. *Arch Phys Med, 30:*286-288, 1949.